HISTORY AND LIFE

4TH EDITION

Workbook
Teacher's Annotated Edition

Textbook by

T. Walter Wallbank, *University of Southern California*

Arnold Schrier, *University of Cincinnati*

Donna Maier, *University of Northern Iowa*

Patricia Guttierez-Smith, *Roberto Clemente High School, Chicago, Illinois*

Scott, Foresman and Company

Editorial Offices: Glenview, Illinois

Regional Sales Offices: Sunnyvale, California • Atlanta, Georgia
Glenview, Illinois • Oakland, New Jersey • Dallas, Texas

ISBN: 0-673-35090-8

5 6 7 8 9 10 - WEB - 999897969594

To the Teacher

This *Workbook* is designed to accompany *History and Life, 4th Edition*. It consists of 164 Worksheets—one Worksheet for each chapter section. These Worksheets are all new and are not available in the *Teacher's Resource File*. They are intended to be used in place of, or as supplements to, the *Activities* in the *Teacher's Resource File*.

The Worksheets review and reinforce the events, concepts, people, and places presented in the text. Worksheet exercises require students to apply critical thinking skills and creativity to their study of world history. As appropriate, the Worksheets include information to complement and enrich the material presented in the pupil text. The Worksheets may be used during and after the study of a chapter section.

Contents

Unit 3   The Era of Regional Civilizations: Christendom and Islam

Unit 4   The Era of Regional Civilizations: Asia, Africa, and the Americas

Unit 5   The Early Modern Era: Europe's Transformation and Expansion

Unit 7   The Sweep of Revolutions in the West

Unit 8   The Interval of Western Dominance

WORKSHEET
Chapter 1, Section 1
Prehistoric People

Part A
Identify which prehistoric people each riddle best describes.

1. Just because I am low-browed doesn't mean that I have a little brain. In fact, my brain was even larger than that of people today. My disappearance from the earth 40,000 years ago remains a mystery. You, however, can solve the mystery of my identity. Who am I?
   Neanderthal

2. Although I may have a Latin name, I am just like you. Who am I?
   Homo sapiens

3. I may have walked upright—but then maybe not. Am I fully human? Scientists prefer to call me humanlike. Who am I?
   australopithecine

4. My brain was twice the size of my predecessor's. I first made use of fire and the hand-ax. Java is one place I definitely lived. Who am I?
   Homo erectus

5. Modern humans probably descend from me. My remains were found in a cave in France. Who am I?
   Cro-Magnon

Part B
Write the letter of the term from the box next to its definition or identifying phrase.

1. __e__ early prehumans, also called "southern apes"
2. __d__ a name meaning "walked upright"
3. __a__ a name meaning "two-legged primates"
4. __c__ home of the earliest life forms
5. __f__ scientists who excavate, classify, and study physical remains of ancient cultures
6. __b__ "intelligent human beings"
7. __h__ scientists likely to estimate the age of the earth
8. __g__ one of the two groups of prehistoric people considered to be *Homo sapiens*

a. hominids	**c.** water	**e.** australopithecines	**g.** Cro-Magnon people
b. *Homo sapiens*	**d.** *Homo erectus*	**f.** archaeologists	**h.** geologists

              1

WORKSHEET
Chapter 1, Section 2

Neanderthal and Cro-Magnon People

In this worksheet you will review some of the ways Neanderthal and Cro-Magnon people ensured their survival.

Part A
Number the events in the order in which they happened.

2 Fire became important to survival.

3 The Ice Age ended.

1 Early prehumans observed fire.

4 The Neolithic period began.

5 The prehistoric period ended with the invention of writing.

Part B
Read the statements below. Write **T** if the statement is true and **F** if it is false. On the lines below, rewrite each false statement to make it true.

1. **F** The Stone Age is called "prehistoric" because the ability to exchange ideas had not yet been invented.

2. **T** Both australopithecines and *Homo erectus* were acquainted with fire.

3. **F** During the first two glacial periods, the Neanderthal people were unable to adapt to changes in climate.

4. **F** There is no evidence to support the hypothesis that the Neanderthal people were religious.

5. **T** Those who could not adapt to the cold conditions of the Ice Age moved, died from exposure, or starved.

6. **T** The inventiveness of the Neanderthal people was a key factor in ensuring their survival during the Ice Age.

7. **F** Cro-Magnon people developed a highly advanced agriculture.

8. **T** It took thousands of years for prehumans to advance from observing fire to using it for cooking food.

1. The Stone Age is called "prehistoric" because writing had not yet been invented.

3. During the first two glacial periods, the Neanderthal people adapted to the cold by wearing animal-skin clothing and using fire.

4. Articles excavated from the graves of Neanderthals support the hypothesis that the Neanderthal people were religious.

7. Cro-Magnon people never developed agriculture, but lived entirely as hunter-gatherers.

WORKSHEET
Chapter 1, Section 3

Life in the Stone Age

Read the clues below and complete the crossword puzzle using the terms in the box.

```
¹M E ²S O L I T H I C    ³C
      P                    O
   ⁴W E A V I N G          M
      C                    M
  ⁵P  I                    U
⁶C U L T I V A T I N G     N      ⁷A        ⁸N
   O  A                    I   ⁹I R R I G A T I O N
   T  L                    T      R        M
   T  I                    I      I        A
   E  Z                    E      C        D
   R  A                    S      U        S
   Y  T                           L
  ¹⁰N E O L I T H I C             T
      I                          U
 ¹¹G O V E R N M E N T S         R
                            ¹²G R A Z I N G
                                 E
```

Across

1. term referring to the Middle Stone Age
4. the process of making cloth from plant fiber
6. working the soil with hoes and stone tools
9. an invention allowing agriculture in dry areas
10. term referring to the New Stone Age
11. systems of ruling society that became more complex among the Neolithic people
12. a kind of land that nomads sought

Down

2. dividing up work so that people can work according to their skills
3. arose after the development of specialization of labor
5. an invention of Mesolithic people that allowed better storage of food and water
7. the deliberate cultivation of crops and the raising of livestock
8. people who travel from pasture to pasture

specialization	governments	irrigation	Mesolithic
weaving	cultivating	nomads	agriculture
Neolithic	grazing	communities	

WORKSHEET

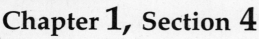

Chapter 1, Section 4

The Bronze Age

In this worksheet you will review the Bronze Age.

Part A

Only three of the four terms in each group below are related in some way.
Circle the term that does not belong and explain how the remaining three
terms are related. The first one has been done as a sample.

1. humiliation   execution   (mutilation)   banishment

   All are examples of common punishments for wrongdoers during the Bronze Age.

2. copper   bronze   tin   (iron)

   Possible answer: Copper and tin were melted together during this age to make bronze.

3. (hunter-gatherers)   plow   dike   agriculture

   Possible answer: The invention of the dike and the plow allowed agriculture to flourish.

4. (cave art)   sled   cart   wheel

   Possible answer: Use of the first sled led to the invention of the wheel, which in turn led to the development of the cart.

5. (nomads)   sailboat   trade   sea routes

   Possible answer: The invention of the sailboat and the development of sea routes allowed trade to grow during the Bronze Age.

Part B

Read the statements below and write **F** for fact or **O** for opinion before each one.
For each opinion, explain one other point of view that people might hold.

1. **O**   Developments in transportation were the most important technological advances of the Bronze Age.

2. **F**   Prehistoric metalworkers found bronze to be more useful than copper alone.

3. **F**   The people of the Fertile Crescent pioneered in the science of metallurgy.

4. **F**   The many inventions of the Bronze Age allowed for the growth of more complex economies.

5. **O**   The development of specialized labor contributed most to the growth of commerce and trade during the Bronze Age.

1. Possible answer: Agricultural advances were the most important since they led to growth in other areas of the economy.

5. Possible answer: Improvements in transportation helped commerce and trade to flourish.

WORKSHEET
Chapter 2, Section 1

In this worksheet you will review some aspects of Mesopotamian civilization.

Civilization of the Mesopotamians

Part A
Only three of the four items in each group are related in some way. Circle the item that does not belong and explain how the remaining three items are related.

1. Tigris and Euphrates rivers   plain of Shinar   (Hammurabi)   Mesopotamia
   Possible answer: The Sumerian civilization developed in Mesopotamia, on the plain of Shinar, between the Tigris and Euphrates rivers.

2. stylus   cuneiform   wedge   (arch)
   Possible answer: The Sumerians used a stylus to make their wedge-shaped writing called cuneiform.

3. ziggurat   city-state   tower   (irrigation)
   Possible answer: In the center of each Sumerian city-state was a massive, stepped tower called a ziggurat.

4. plow   arch   (calendar)   wheeled vehicles
   Possible answer: The Sumerians were the first to invent the plow and arch and were probably the first to use wheeled vehicles.

5. (Sargon I)   Hammurabi   legal code   harsh punishments
   Possible answer: Hammurabi's legal codes provided for harsh punishments, particularly for crimes committed by commoners against aristocrats.

Part B
Imagine that Hammurabi had buried a time capsule to give future generations a clear picture of the way his people lived. What things might he have included in his time capsule?
Possible answer: a copy of his code of laws; a description or map of his empire; clay bricks; a stylus and clay tablets; clothes; drawings of families, foods, methods of farming, transportation, architectural elements, and buildings; and examples of mathematics and literature

WORKSHEET
Chapter 2, Section 2

The Early Egyptians

In this worksheet you
will review important
developments in
Egyptian history.

Part A
Number the events in the order in which they happened.

__6__ The last Egyptian dynasty was overthrown by the Greeks.

__5__ Egypt reached the height of its power under Thutmose III.

__1__ The world's first solar calendar was invented.

__3__ The Hyksos invaded and conquered Egypt.

__2__ King Menes united Upper and Lower Egypt.

__4__ The restoration of Egyptian rule began the New Kingdom.

Part B
Complete each statement with explanations given in your text.

1. The development of irrigation by Egyptian farmers may be regarded as an early form of local government **because**
   Possible answer: work-team leaders and administrators had the power to direct the work of planting and harvesting.

2. Egypt was well protected from invasion **because**
   Possible answer: deserts, cataracts, and the Mediterranean provided natural barriers, leaving only northeast Egypt exposed to invaders.

3. Despite the humiliation of Hyksos rule, the Egyptians benefited in some ways from the invaders **because**
   Possible answer: the Hyksos introduced them to superior bows and arrows and to the use of the horse-drawn chariot in waging war.

4. The Nile flood was a welcome event to the Egyptians **because**
   Possible answer: it brought fertile deposits of silt to the land.

5. Throughout much of Egyptian history, the pharaohs had absolute power over their subjects **because**
   Possible answer: people believed the pharaohs were descended from a god and were gods themselves.

6. Egyptian priests succeeded in persuading Egyptians to return to polytheism after Akhenaton's death **because**
   Possible answer: they convinced the people that if they practiced monotheism, they would suffer the wrath of the gods.

WORKSHEET

Chapter 2, Section 3

In this worksheet you will review the Indus Valley civilization.

The Indus Valley Civilization

Part A

Write **C** next to each phrase that correctly completes the unfinished sentence. (Each incomplete sentence may have more than one correct ending.)

1. People of the Indus Valley developed a complex civilization that

   C had well-planned cities.

   C covered an area of about 1,000 miles

   C had a uniform administration over several towns.

   _____ had the world's first solar calendar.

   C had a standardized system of weights.

2. The economy of the Indus Valley civilization was

   C based on farming and trade.

   C highly productive, as evidenced by the size of the uniform weights for grain.

   C enriched by trade with Sumerians, Babylonians, and Mesopotamians.

   _____ based on cattle as a symbol of wealth.

3. The Indus Valley civilization slowly declined as

   C Mohenjo-Daro was repeatedly overrun by mud.

   C constant rebuilding reduced the will and energy of the people.

   _____ trade with other civilizations was ordered to stop.

   C an unknown disaster struck about 1500 B.C.

Part B

On a separate piece of paper, write a letter that an archaeologist might have written to a friend shortly after the discovery of Mohenjo-Daro. Your letter should show the significance of at least four findings. Before writing your letter, fill out the chart below to help organize your ideas.

Finding	Significance
Possible answers:	
uniform weights	strong central government
piers	city's location on water
statues of females	worship of a goddess
granary	productive agriculture
sewage system	engineering skills

WORKSHEET

Chapter 2, Section 4
Early China

In this worksheet you will review the Chinese civilization that developed along the Huang River.

Part A

For each set of statements below, write **M** before the main idea and **S** before statements that support or help explain the main idea. One statement in each set is not related to the main idea; write **X** next to this statement.

Set 1

__S__ According to legend, Yu fought a mighty river to save his people from floods.

__X__ Loess is a fine, rich soil.

__S__ Ban Ku used a hammer and chisel to make the universe.

__M__ The Chinese have many myths and legends about ancient times.

Set 2

__X__ The Chang River is also known as the Yangtze.

__M__ Geography influenced early Chinese civilization.

__S__ The Huang River, called "China's Sorrow," brought life as well as destruction to its valley.

__S__ The fertile Huang River plains provided productive farming, including the growing of millet.

Set 3

__M__ Although nobles controlled the distant parts of the kingdom, the Shang king was a powerful leader.

__S__ In addition to being the military leader, the Shang king was the high priest.

__X__ The Chinese during the Shang dynasty had a polytheistic religion.

__S__ The people believed the king governed by the command of heaven.

Part B

Write the letter of the term or name from the box next to its definition or identifying phrase.

1. __b__ oldest collection of Chinese poetry

2. __d__ best known product of Shang artisans

3. __e__ used to foretell the future

4. __g__ main economic activity of Chinese during the Shang period

5. __h__ river along which early Chinese first grew millet

6. __a__ artificial pools for cultivation of rice

7. __c__ river along which early Chinese first grew rice

8. __f__ skill advanced by Chinese women

a. paddies
b. *Book of Odes*
c. Chang
d. bronze work
e. bones and shells
f. silkworm cultivation
g. farming
h. Huang

WORKSHEET
Chapter 3, Section 1

In this worksheet you will review the culture of the Phoenicians.

Phoenician Culture

Part A
Write the letter of the word or phrase from the box that best completes each sentence.

1. __b__ The Phoenicians sailed around _____ about 2,000 years before Vasco da Gama did.

2. __c__ An outgrowth of their trading activities, one of the Phoenicians' most lasting contributions to later cultures was the development of the _____.

3. __e__ The Phoenicians lived in what is now the country of _____.

4. __f__ The Phoenicians sailed west out of the Mediterranean Sea into the _____ as far north as Britain.

5. __g__ The Phoenicians never formed a united nation, but lived in _____ like the Sumerians.

6. __d__ The Phoenicians were a branch of the Semitic people known as _____.

7. __a__ The Phoenicians spread _____ to Greece, Africa, Italy, and Spain.

a. Mesopotamian and Egyptian culture
b. Africa
c. alphabet
d. Canaanites
e. Lebanon
f. Atlantic Ocean
g. city-states

Part B
Write **T** if the statement is true and **F** if it is false. On the lines below, rewrite each false statement to make it true.

1. __F__ Phoenicia rose to prominence before the Egyptian civilization reached its height.

2. __T__ The Phoenicians became the greatest traders, shipbuilders, navigators, and colonizers of the Mediterranean region.

3. __T__ The Phoenicians developed the art of navigating by the stars.

4. __F__ The Phoenician alphabet used pictures to represent words.

5. __F__ The alphabet we use today is an adaptation of the Phoenician alphabet, with no additions.

1. Possible answer: Phoenicia flourished between 1200 and 300 B.C., after the decline of Egypt.

4. Possible answer: The Phoenician alphabet used signs to represent sounds.

5. Possible answer: The alphabet we use today is an adaptation of the Phoenician alphabet, which developed consonants, and the Greek alphabet, which developed vowels.

WORKSHEET
Chapter 3, Section 2

The Jewish Culture

In this worksheet you will review the development of the Jewish culture.

Part A

For each set of statements below, write **M** before the main idea and **S** before statements that support or help explain the main idea. One statement in each set is not related to the main idea; write **X** next to this statement.

Set 1

S   Moses brought the Ten Commandments to his people.

M   Moses was a major figure in the development of the Jewish faith.

S   During the Exodus, Moses taught the Israelites that they had made an eternally binding covenant, or formal agreement, with God.

X   Joshua defeated the Canaanites.

Set 2

M   From Abraham's time, the Israelites worshiped one God.

S   Among the laws introduced by Moses was a commandment requiring the worship of one God.

X   Many Israelites in Canaan adopted the gods of the Canaanites.

S   Solomon built the first temple to one God.

Set 3

M   Judaism was refined by a series of great prophets.

X   Moses led his people in the Exodus from Egypt.

S   Isaiah declared that Israel was God's "righteous servant," purified by suffering and ready to guide the world to the worship of the one supreme God.

S   Jeremiah taught that God demanded righteousness and protection for the weak and helpless.

Set 4

S   The stories of the Jewish kings are told in the Bible.

S   The Bible tells about the Exodus from Egypt.

X   Archaeology can tell us much about the history of the Middle East.

M   Early Jewish history is recorded in the Bible.

Part B

Number the events in the order in which they happened.

6   The Chaldeans conquer the southern kingdom.

5   The Assyrians conquer the northern kingdom.

4   Israel reaches the peak of its political power under Solomon.

2   The Exodus from Egypt takes place.

3   Saul becomes first king of Israel.

1   Abraham leads his people into Canaan.

WORKSHEET
Chapter 3, Section 3

In this worksheet you will review the Assyrian, Chaldean, and Persian cultures.

Assyrians, Chaldeans, and Persians

Part A
Write **A** if the statement refers to the Assyrians, **C** if it refers to the Chaldeans, and **P** if it refers to the Persians.

1. __P__ Their government was ruled by despots, but they treated their subject peoples humanely.

2. __A__ Their rule was one of the cruelest in the ancient world.

3. __C__ They made significant contributions to astronomy.

4. __A__ They conducted mass deportations among conquered peoples to destroy national feeling and to prevent uprisings.

5. __C__ Nebuchadnezzar built a temple-tower to their chief god.

6. __P__ Cyrus the Great led their army against the Medes.

7. __A__ Their empire fell to the Neo-Babylonians.

8. __C__ They built the famous Hanging Gardens of Babylon.

9. __C__ They were also called Neo-Babylonians.

10. __A__ They had perhaps the most impressive army in the ancient world, including chariots and mounted cavalry.

11. __P__ They had horsemen who could travel 1,500 miles in a little more than a week.

12. __C__ They believed that by studying the stars they could predict the future.

Part B
Write a paragraph describing the accomplishments of the Chaldeans. Use the following words in your paragraph: *Fertile Crescent, Nebuchadnezzar, Assyrians, Babylon, Hanging Gardens, Tower of Babel, mathematics, astronomy, astrology.*

Example: The Chaldeans, under their king *Nebuchadnezzar*, built the Chaldean Empire by conquering the *Fertile Crescent* and taking over many of the lands ruled previously by the *Assyrians*. Nebuchadnezzar rebuilt *Babylon*, constructing the *Hanging Gardens* and a ziggurat in honor of the chief god of the Chaldeans; some scholars believe this ziggurat was the *Tower of Babel*. The Chaldeans made important contributions to *astronomy* by using *mathematics* to work out detailed tables of the movements of the heavenly bodies. The Chaldeans also believed they could predict the future by studying the stars and thus began the study of *astrology*.

WORKSHEET
Chapter 4, Section 1

In this worksheet you
will review events in the
history of Crete, Mycenae,
and Troy.

Early Aegean Civilization

Part A

Some of the following sentences describe the Minoan civilization of Crete, some the Mycenaean civilization, and some the Trojan civilization. Write **C** if the statement refers to Crete, **M** if to Mycenae, and **T** if to Troy.

1. __T__ The Roman poet Vergil described its fall in the *Aeneid*.
2. __C__ This civilization developed on an island southeast of Greece.
3. __T__ This city controlled trade between the Aegean and Black seas.
4. __C__ This culture took its name from King Minos.
5. __M__ This civilization was developed by people from the Caspian Sea region.
6. __C__ This was the first of the three early Aegean civilizations to develop.
7. __T__ The home of this society was modern-day Turkey in Asia Minor.
8. __M__ The people of this culture borrowed a great deal from the Minoans.
9. __C__ Bull dancing was a sport for members of this society.
10. __C__ Archaeologist Sir Arthur Evans uncovered its ruins.
11. __M__ Soldiers from this civilization owed their victory over their rivals to a wooden horse.
12. __M__ Attacks on the Minoans by this civilization led to the capture of Knossos.
13. __C__ One of this culture's famous legends was the story of Theseus and his travels through the labyrinth.
14. __T__ The Greek poet Homer described the war between this society and Mycenae in the *Iliad*.
15. __M__ From 1400 to 1200 B.C., this civilization was a unifying force in Greece and on the Aegean islands.

Part B

Number the events in the order in which they happened.

__2__ The Mycenaeans capture the royal city of Crete.
__3__ The Mycenaeans are driven out of Crete.
__5__ Homer writes the *Iliad* and *Odyssey*.
__4__ War between Mycenae and Troy ends.
__1__ Neolithic people come to Crete.
__6__ Vergil writes the *Aeneid* based on Greek sources.

WORKSHEET

Chapter 4, Section 2

In this worksheet you will review the development of Greek democracy.

Greek Democracy Develops

Part A

Write **T** if the statement is true and **F** if it is false. On the lines below, rewrite each false statement to make it true.

1. __T__ The geography of Greece contributed to the growth of city-states.

2. __T__ Democratic government gradually evolved in most Greek city-states.

3. __F__ Solon reduced the powers of the Council of 400 in Athens.

4. __T__ According to Pericles, the Greeks viewed public debate as an important part of decision making by the leaders of the state.

5. __F__ In Sparta the first step toward democracy was the creation of the assembly of citizens.

6. __F__ Helots had the rights of citizens in Sparta.

3. Possible answer: Solon enlarged the council to include rich property owners.

5. Possible answer: Sparta was not a democracy; the citizens' assembly had no real power, and the Council of Elders controlled the state.

6. Possible answer: The helots were looked upon as state property and were treated little better than slaves.

Part B

In a speech made in 431 B.C., Pericles said that Athenian citizens considered public service to be an honorable and necessary part of every citizen's life. What are some ways Americans today serve the public?

Possible answer: Americans today serve as elected officials and government workers at the local, state, and national levels; some work or volunteer in social service programs that provide aid to various groups within the local community; others belong to religious or social organizations that work to better the community.

Do you think public service is as important to Americans today as it was to Athenian citizens at the time Pericles made his speech? Give reasons for your answer.

Students answering "yes" might point to the many charitable organizations in most communities and to the number of people who run for political office. Those answering "no" might point to the low voter turnout of Americans in some elections.

Name _____ Date _____

WORKSHEET

Chapter 4, Section 3

Athenian Civilization

In this worksheet you will review Athens' war with Persia and examine some principles of Athenian democracy.

Part A
Complete each statement with the explanations given in your text.

1. The Greeks came into conflict with the Persians **because**
Possible answer: Greeks colonized and traded in areas close to the Persian Empire.

2. The Ionian Greeks were angered by Darius' reorganization of the Persian Empire **because**
Possible answer: they felt that they had been given a lesser role in the empire and resented Persian rule.

3. The Persians attacked Athens **because**
Possible answer: they wanted to conquer the Greek mainland and punish the Athenians for helping the Ionians.

4. The Athenians defeated the Persians at the battle of Marathon **because**
Possible answer: the Athenians had better weapons and military strategy.

5. The Peloponnesian War erupted **because**
Possible answer: Sparta and the other city-states resented Athenian control of the Delian League.

Part B
Although Athens is generally regarded as the world's first democracy, not everyone agrees on exactly how democratic Athenian democracy was. Read the statements below and write **F** for fact and **O** for opinion before each one. For each opinion, explain one other point of view that people might hold.

1. __F__ In Athens all citizens had the right to hold office and participate in their government.

2. __O__ Athenian democracy provides a good example of pure democracy.

3. __O__ By requiring that a man on trial be judged by a jury of as large as 2,000 jurors, the Athenians carried the principle of mass political participation to absurd lengths.

4. __F__ The existence of the assembly in Athens supports the view that Greece was a direct democracy.

2. Possible answer: Athenian democracy could be described as pure only for the minority who were citizens.

3. Possible answer: By setting up very large juries, the Athenians assured fair trials and equal rights for all citizens.

WORSHEET

WORKSHEET
Chapter 4, Section 4

In this worksheet you will review the main events leading to the end of the Hellenic Age.

The Macedonian Conquest

Part A

Using the numbers **1** through **4**, arrange the events in each set in chronological order.

1. __2__ Athens and Thebes form an alliance against Macedonia.

    __4__ Philip gains control of the Greek peninsula, excluding Sparta.

    __3__ The Macedonian and Greek armies fight the battle of Chaeronea.

    __1__ King Philip organizes Macedonia into city-states and creates a standing army.

2. __1__ The major Greek city-states form the Hellenic League.

    __2__ Philip of Macedonia is assassinated.

    __4__ Alexander's armies defeat the forces of Darius III.

    __3__ Alexander the Great gains a foothold in Asia after his victory at the battle of Granicus.

3. __4__ The Hellenistic Age lasts for 200 years.

    __3__ Alexander's empire is divided into three parts.

    __2__ Alexander dies of fever in Babylon.

    __1__ Two hundred years of Persian domination of the eastern Mediterranean world end.

Part B

Imagine that you are a citizen of Athens living at the time of Alexander the Great. Write a paragraph explaining how you feel about Alexander's conquests, considering both the advantages and disadvantages for your city.

Possible answer: We Athenians are proud to see Greek language, culture, and law spread to faraway parts of the world. However, we feel regret and humiliation at our loss of power and independence.

WORKSHEET
Chapter 5, Section 1
Greek Philosophy

Part A
Write the term or name from the box that best completes each statement.

1. A famous school in Athens that was started by Plato and existed for over 900 years was the ___Academy___.

2. The discipline that seeks to understand the universe and the individual's place within it is called ___philosophy___.

3. The work of Plato that describes an imaginary land where each man and woman performs the task to which he or she is best suited is ___The Republic___.

4. Asking the right questions and systematically seeking answers is ___inquiry___.

5. The school of philosophy whose founder believed in increasing pleasure by avoiding extremes was ___Epicureanism___.

6. The philosophy which taught that true happiness comes when one finds one's proper place in nature was ___Stoicism___.

7. The philosopher who taught the Doctrine of the Mean was ___Aristotle___.

philosophy	*The Republic*	inquiry	Epicureanism
Academy	Stoicism	Aristotle	

Part B
Complete each statement with the explanations given in your text.

1. Socrates was known as "the gadfly" **because**
   Possible answer: his persistent questioning stung his listeners into thinking.

2. Socrates was put on trial **because**
   Possible answer: some Athenians believed he corrupted youth by encouraging them to question the acts of civic leaders.

3. Socrates advocated a persistent questioning of all ideas **because**
   Possible answer: he believed that by carefully analyzing the answers one could arrive at the truth.

4. Compared to Plato, Aristotle seemed more down-to-earth **because**
   Possible answer: unlike Plato, he dealt with practical issues rather than abstract ideas.

WORKSHEET
Chapter 5, Section 2

Greek Literature

In this worksheet you will review Greek literature of the Golden Age.

Read the clues below and complete the crossword puzzle using the terms in the box.

```
 1        2              3        4
 H E R O D O T U S       S        A
         R               O        R
         A               P        I        5
         M             6 H I S T O R Y      T
         A               O        T         R
     7                   C        O         A
     E               8   L        P         G
     U               A   E        H         E
     R               E            A         D
   9 D I O N Y S U S  S U S       N         Y
     P               C            S
     I               H        10
     D               Y         O E D I P U S
     E               L            S
     S            11 T H U C Y D I D E S
                     S
```

Across

1. author of *History of the Persian Wars*

6. the subject about which Thucydides wrote

9. Greek god of wine

10. central character in a play by Sophocles

11. historian who looked for human causes of the Greek wars

Down

2. type of Greek literature

3. author of *Oedipus Rex*

4. writer of Greek comedy

5. form of drama in which endings are unhappy or disastrous

7. last of three great Athenian tragedians

8. father of tragedy

drama	history	Euripides	tragedy
Aristophanes	Dionysus	Aeschylus	Herodotus
Oedipus	Sophocles	Thucydides	

WORSHEET

Chapter 5, Section 3

In this worksheet you
will review Greek
achievements in science
and art.

Greek Science and Art

Part A

Only three of the four items in each group are related in some way. Circle the item
that does not belong and explain how the remaining three items are related.

1. Euclid   (astronomy)   geometry   Pythagoras

   Possible answer: Both Euclid and Pythagoras were known for their
   work in the field of geometry.

2. oath   (Archimedes)   Hippocrates   medicine

   Possible answer: In the field of medicine, the name of Hippocrates is
   still associated with an oath of ethical conduct for physicians.

3. (Alexandria)   drawings   pottery   paintings

   Possible answer: Greek pottery is famous not only in its own right,
   but also for the drawings and paintings on the vases.

4. Phidias   Athena   (pottery)   sculpture

   Possible answer: Phidias is famous for his sculpture, particularly for
   his masterpiece—Athena.

5. "Laocoon"   "Apollo Belvedere"   "Winged Victory"   (Corinthian painting)

   "Laocoon," "Apollo Belvedere," and "Winged Victory" are examples
   of outstanding sculpture that survive from the Hellenistic Age.

Part B

For each set of statements below, write **M** for the main idea and **S** before statements
that support or help explain the main idea. One statement in each set is not related
to the main idea; write **X** next to this statement.

1. __S__ Aristotle argued that new truths could
   be acquired through induction
   and deduction.

   __X__ The Greek scientist Hippocrates founded
   a medical school.

   __S__ This new breed of philosophers believed
   that direct study and observation enabled
   one to find the truth.

   __M__ During the Hellenistic Age, Greek
   philosopher-scientists introduced new
   methods of scientific inquiry.

2. __S__ The mathematical breakthroughs of
   Euclid form the foundation of plane
   and solid geometry.

   __X__ Only parts of the work of Phidias
   still remain.

   __M__ Greek scientists made important
   discoveries that advanced human
   knowledge.

   __S__ Archimedes discovered the method of
   water displacement to measure volume.

   __S__ High-school students today study the
   Pythagorean theorem.

WORKSHEET
Chapter 6, Section 1
Early Roman History

In this worksheet you will review important events in the early history of Rome.

Part A

Using the numbers **1** through **7**, arrange the events in chronological order. On the lines after each event, tell why it was an important happening.

a. __4__ The Gauls invade Rome.
Possible answer: Their attack damaged Roman prestige but led the Romans to fortify their army.

b. __7__ Pyrrhus leads attack against Rome.
Possible answer: His attack was a pyrrhic victory, so costly that Pyrrhus returned to Greece.

c. __1__ The Roman Senate sets up a republic.
Possible answer: This set up the machinery of government for Rome—two consuls and the Senate.

d. __3__ Plebeians win the right to have written laws.
Possible answer: This prevented judges from unfairly ruling against the plebeians to serve patrician interests.

e. __2__ Rome forms the Latin League with Latin tribes.
Possible answer: This allowed for successful control of the central Italian peninsula.

f. __6__ The plebeian assembly wins the right to make laws for all citizens.
Possible answer: Plebeians' exercise of the veto led senators to rethink unpopular legislation.

g. __5__ Members of the Latin League revolt against Rome.
Possible answer: The revolt led to the league's disbandment and Rome's conquest of its former allies.

Part B

Write the number of each event from Part A and its exact date on the proper place on the time line.

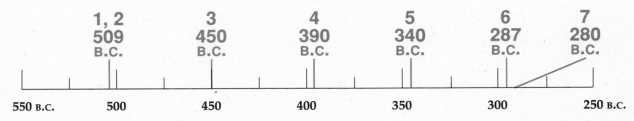

1, 2	3	4	5	6	7
509	450	390	340	287	280
B.C.	B.C.	B.C.	B.C.	B.C.	B.C.

550 B.C.   500   450   400   350   300   250 B.C.

WORKSHEET
Chapter 6, Section 2

In this worksheet you will review the ways in which Rome changed from a republic to an empire.

From Republic to Empire

Part A

For each statement below, write two or three sentences that support or provide details for that statement.

1. Rome's greatest rival in the region of northern Africa was Carthage.
   Possible answer: A rich and powerful trading city with a strong navy, Carthage fought three major wars with Rome between 264 and 146 B.C. Despite Carthage's greater supply of gold, manpower, and ships, Rome defeated Carthage.

2. As Rome expanded, political and economic changes at home led to civil war.
   Possible answer: As the Senate's political power grew, government corruption increased. Economic changes created an impoverished farming class and a class of wealthy, self-interested landowners. Rivalry between the two classes erupted into civil war.

3. Julius Caesar used his popularity with the plebeians and the army to take control of Rome.
   Possible answer: From 58 to 51 B.C., Caesar led the army in the Gallic wars, gaining popularity with the masses. He defied the Senate's order to return to Rome without his army. After defeating his enemies, he became dictator.

4. Octavian became the first emperor of Rome.
   Possible answer: Octavian united Rome under one ruler after a century of Roman civil war. Although he observed the forms of republican government, Octavian kept the final power in his own hands. First called *imperator*, later he was given the title *Augustus*.

Part B

What do you think might have happened in Rome if Julius Caesar had NOT crossed the Rubicon? Write a paragraph explaining your answer.
Students' answers may note that conditions of plebeian unrest made Rome ripe for political change. The discontented masses who had joined the army were willing to extend their loyalty to a strong leader. Another military figure, such as Pompey, might have taken control. If a strong leader had not emerged, a Rome weakened by civil strife might have fallen to outside enemies.

WORKSHEET

Chapter 6, Section 3

The Roman Empire

Read the statements below and write **F** for fact and **O** for opinion before each one. For each opinion, explain one other point of view that people might hold.

1. __O__ Augustus was the greatest emperor of Rome.

2. __O__ The *Pax Romana* was a peaceful period during which people lived happily under enlightened Roman rule.

3. __O__ Rome declined primarily for economic reasons.

4. __O__ Both Diocletian and Constantine were humane despots.

5. __F__ After the death of Theodosius I, the Roman Empire was divided into eastern and western halves.

6. __O__ The Roman emperor's decision to reduce the gold and silver content of the money supply was wise, since it saved the empire's dwindling supply of precious metal.

7. __F__ The following words of Marcus Aurelius reflect the influence of the Stoic philosophy: "Blot out vain pomp; check impulse; quench appetite; keep reason under its own control."

8. __O__ Had Romans followed the Stoic philosophy, the decline of Rome could have been prevented.

1. **Possible answer: Trajan, Hadrian, or Marcus Aurelius was the greatest emperor of Rome.**

2. **Possible answer: The *Pax Romana* was a peaceful period, but not everyone was happy; for example, the Jewish people probably resented Roman persecution.**

3. **Possible answer: The primary reason for Rome's decline was political instability.**

4. **Possible answer: Neither Diocletian nor Constantine could be called humane in light of their extensive use of the secret police.**

6. **Possible answer: The decision to devalue coins was unwise because it led to inflation.**

8. **Possible answer: The decline of Rome was due to many long-standing problems, not all of which could have been alleviated by applying Stoic principles.**

_____

_____

WORKSHEET
Chapter 6, Section 4

The Roman Heritage

Part A
Present at least two specific facts from your text to support each statement.

1. Latin's lasting influence is evident in the words people use today.
   Possible answer: Modern Romance languages developed from the vernacular form of Latin. Many languages are written in the Roman alphabet. English has thousands of words of Latin origin.

2. Roman law provided the basis for many systems of law today.
   Possible answer: Legal codes based on Roman law are still in use in Italy, France, Spain, and Latin America. The Romans established the legal principles of judicial precedent and the tradition of written laws.

3. The classical culture was a blend of Greek and Roman culture.
   Possible answer: The Romans admired Hellenistic culture and borrowed heavily from the Greeks. When the Romans borrowed, they modified and adapted Greek culture.

4. The Romans did not slavishly copy Greek art and architecture.
   Possible answer: Roman architecture was more elaborate and secular than Greek. Roman sculpture was more lifelike. Unlike the Greeks, Romans used domes and vaults in their buildings.

Part B
Write the letter of the name of the person from the box that best matches the description.

1. __c__ author of a history of Rome
2. __f__ a scholar, astronomer, and mapmaker
3. __d__ author of a study of Germanic tribes
4. __a__ author of *Commentaries on the Gallic Wars*
5. __b__ author of the *Aeneid*
6. __g__ physician who studied the role of the arteries
7. __e__ author of *Parallel Lives*

a. Julius Caesar	e. Plutarch
b. Vergil	f. Ptolemy
c. Livy	g. Galen
d. Tacitus	

WORKSHEET
Chapter 7, Section 1
India's Geography

In this worksheet you will review the geography of India and its influence on Indian history.

Part A
Write the letter of the name or term from the box next to its identifying phrase.

1. __h__ the gateway used by India's invaders
2. __a__ a country once included in ancient India
3. __f__ the river system where one of the world's first civilizations began
4. __g__ the river system that runs from the Himalayas to the Bay of Bengal
5. __d__ the wet season in India
6. __e__ the dry season in India
7. __b__ the region of India subject to extremes of temperature
8. __c__ one result of summer monsoons carrying too much moisture

a. Pakistan	**c.** famine	**e.** winter	**g.** Ganges
b. northern plains	**d.** summer	**f.** Indus	**h.** Khyber Pass

Part B
Only three of the four items in each group are related. Circle the item that does not belong and explain how the remaining three items are related. The first one has been done as a sample.

1. harsh climate   high mountains   (good harbors)   immense deserts
   All are geographical features of India.
   _____

2. (Bay of Bengal)   "Mother"   sacred river   Ganges
   Possible answer: The Ganges is called "Mother" because it is the sacred river of India.

3. wet summers   monsoons   extremes of heat   (winter flooding)
   Possible answer: The three terms characterize India's climate.
   _____

4. barriers to invasion   Himalayas   (Khyber Pass)   Hindu Kush
   Possible answer: Both the Himalaya and the Hindu Kush mountains have acted as barriers to invasion.

5. India   (Burma)   Pakistan   Bangladesh
   Possible answer: India, Pakistan, and Bangladesh were all once part of ancient India.

WORKSHEET
Chapter 7, Section 2

In this worksheet you will review terms relating to life in ancient India.

The Heritage of Ancient India

Read the clues below and complete the crossword puzzle using the terms in the box.

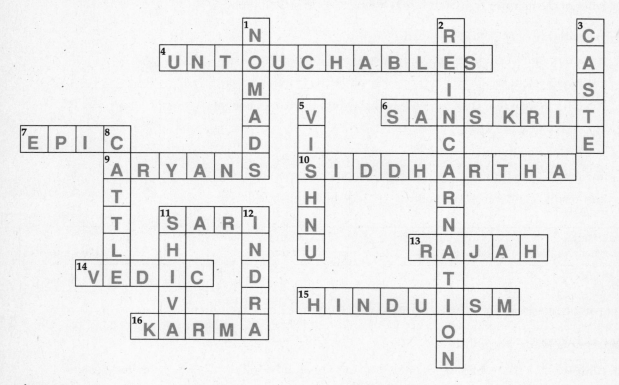

Across

4. on the lowest rank of the caste system

6. language of India

7. a long story-poem on heroic subjects

9. invaders who came through the mountain passes into India about 1500 B.C.

10. the man who founded Buddhism

11. a garment worn by Indian women

13. a petty king in the Indian city-state

14. the age of Aryan-influenced civilization in India

15. the dominant Indian religion

16. Hindu belief that one's future life depends on one's present behavior

Down

1. people who wandered with their herds

2. the belief that people assume a new body after death

3. rigid social rules separating people

5. the Preserver in Hinduism

8. the measure of wealth among the Aryans

11. the Destroyer in Hinduism

12. warrior-god of thunder and battle

epic	nomads	Siddhartha	caste	Indra	reincarnation
Shiva	Sanskrit	rajah	Vishnu	cattle	untouchables
karma	Hinduism	Aryans	sari		

© Scott, Foresman and Company

WORKSHEET
Chapter 7, Section 3

Early Indian History

In this worksheet you will review important events of the Mauryan, Greek, and Kushan periods.

Part A
Write the letter from the time line that matches the date of the event.

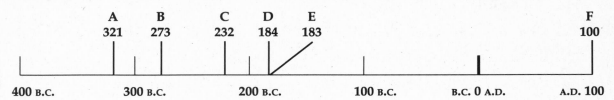

	A	B	C	D	E	F
	321	273	232	184	183	100

400 B.C.   300 B.C.   200 B.C.   100 B.C.   B.C. 0 A.D.   A.D. 100

1. __F__ Kushans invaded India.
2. __A__ Chandragupta Maurya seized one of India's northern kingdoms.
3. __C__ Asoka died.
4. __E__ Demetrius, king of Bactria, conquered northern India.
5. __B__ Asoka became emperor.
6. __D__ The last Mauryan emperor was assassinated.

Part B
Write the word from the box that best completes each statement.

1. Chandragupta Maurya established the Mauryan Empire, but his grandson, __Asoka__, was the most important ruler of that period.

2. Asoka's new religion was __Buddhism__—perhaps one reason for his refusal to make war.

3. The eastern part of Alexander's empire was the kingdom of __Bactria__.

4. In 183 B.C. the __Greeks__ once again conquered much of northern India.

5. By 130 B.C. the ruling class of Bactria was Greek, but its majority population was __Indian__.

6. After the fall of Greek rule, the __Kushans__ reigned over northwestern India and expanded their rule to present-day Afghanistan.

Buddhism	Bactria	Greeks
Asoka	Kushans	Indian

WORKSHEET
Chapter 7, Section 4

The Spread of Indian Culture

In this worksheet
you will review the
"Indianization" of
Southeast Asia.

Part A
Fill in the blanks with the terms or names from the box that best complete
the sentences.

mythology
Sanskrit
local customs
Buddhist
Angkor Wat
culture

1. Where Indian influence was strongest in Southeast Asia, the
_____**culture**_____ became almost Indian.

2. Where Indian influence was weaker in Southeast Asia, it blended
with ____**local customs**____ .

3. The world's largest _____**Buddhist**_____ shrine was built in Java in
the 8th or 9th century.

4. Hindus began to construct one of the greatest religious buildings in the
world, the temple of _____**Angkor Wat**_____ .

5. Local rulers adopted the _____**Sanskrit**_____ language and
Indian ____**mythology**____ .

Part B
Most decisions or actions reflect a people's values: that is, their priorities, or what
they see as important. Choose from the list of values in the box those that best fit
each group and write them on the lines.

Values of the Gupta rulers:
**economic prosperity; advanced learning, literature, and art;
humaneness in penal codes**

Values of Buddhism:
popular education; dignity of common people

Values of Indians during the tenth century:
isolation; superiority of one's own culture

popular education	economic prosperity
superiority of one's own culture	isolation
advanced learning, literature, and art	dignity of common people
humaneness in penal codes	

WORKSHEET
Chapter 8, Section 1

In this worksheet you will review China's major geographical features.

The Geography of China

Part A

Label the map of China below with each geographical feature listed in the box.
Draw in the rivers. Refer to the map titled "Ancient China" in the chapter.

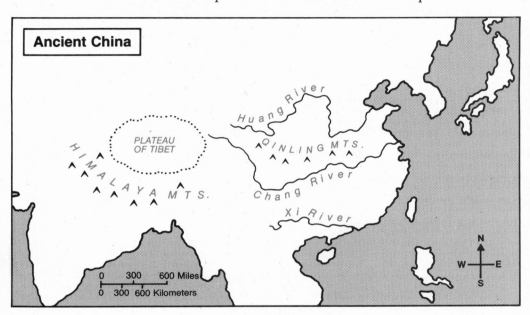

| Himalaya Mountains | Qin Ling Mountains | Chang River |
| Plateau of Tibet | Huang River | Xi River |

Part B

Select the term from the box above that best completes each statement.

1. Because it is navigable for several hundred miles, the
   _____**Chang River**_____ became one of early China's main trade routes.

2. China was protected from invasion in the west by the **Himalaya Mountains**
   and the ____**Plateau of Tibet**____.

3. Good soil for farming was a cause of early development in the basin
   of the ____**Huang River**____.

4. Different parts of China were isolated from one another by natural
   features like the ____**Qin Ling Mountains**____.

5. The valley of the ____**Xi River**____ has the kind of warm, wet
   climate suitable for growing rice year-round.

WORKSHEET

Chapter 8, Section 2

Zhou Achievements

Part A

The list below is of changes that took place in China during the Zhou dynasty. Classify each change by writing **P** for political, **M** for military, and **S** for social. Use the classification that best describes each practice.

1. __M__ invention of catapults

2. __P__ disintegration of feudal states

3. __S__ population growth

4. __P__ emergence of strong nobles

5. __S__ forced labor of farmers on projects for government or local nobility

6. __P__ development of the concept of the Mandate of Heaven

7. __S__ widened disparity between the rich and the poor

8. __M__ invention of cast-iron weapons

9. __P__ selection of officials based on merit rather than social status

Part B

Imagine you are a Chinese person living during the Zhou period. Write a diary entry about the changes that have taken place in China since the Zhous came to power.

Students' answers could mention the development of Confucianism and Taoism; "the Mandate of Heaven" theory of government; changes in art, literature, and the system of writing.

_____

_____

_____

_____

_____

_____

_____

_____

_____

_____

_____

_____

_____

WORKSHEET
Chapter 8, Section 3

Qin and Han China

Part A
Number the events in the order in which they happened. Next to each number, write the letter from the time line that matches the date of the event.

1. __5C__ Wu Di's soldiers push encroaching nomads back from the Great Wall and take over part of Korea.

2. __7D__ The Chinese invent paper.

3. __2C__ Shi Huangdi orders the destruction of Confucian writings.

4. __8D__ Trade with the Kushan Empire brings Buddhism to China.

5. __1C__ The ruler of the state of Qin seizes power in China and begins a dynasty that gives China its name.

6. __6D__ The yoke, or shoulder collar for draft animals, is invented.

7. __4C__ Civil war breaks out in China, and the Han dynasty takes control.

8. __3C__ Construction of the Great Wall of China begins.

| | A | B | C | D | E | F |

1500 B.C.   1000   500   B.C. 0 A.D.   500   1000   A.D. 1500

Part B
Using complete sentences, explain China's advances under the Han dynasty in each of the following areas.

1. inventions
   The Chinese invented paper and a yoke for animals.

2. writings
   Scholars wrote one of the world's first dictionaries and compiled a complete history of Chinese civilization.

3. trade
   The Silk Road ran from China to the Mediterranean Sea, expanding China's trade and increasing contact with outsiders.

4. religion
   Contact with Kushan traders brought Buddhism to China, where the religion quickly spread.

WORKSHEET
Chapter 8, Section 4

The Golden Age of China

Part A
Write **C** next to each phrase that correctly completes the unfinished sentence. (Each incomplete sentence may have more than one correct ending.)

1. In the period between the end of the Han dynasty and the beginning of the Tang dynasty,
   a. __C__ China went through a period of chaos.
   b. _____ literature flourished.
   c. _____ the Great Wall was repaired.
   d. __C__ nomad invaders took control of northern China.
   e. __C__ China was broken into warring kingdoms.

2. Taizong's rule was a great period for China because Taizong
   a. __C__ united warring factions.
   b. __C__ enlarged China's borders.
   c. __C__ instituted tax relief.
   d. _____ instituted the first civil service examinations.
   e. _____ did not follow the Mandate of Heaven.

3. China greatly influenced other countries, particularly because of its
   a. __C__ high-quality schools.
   b. __C__ well-respected, orderly government.
   c. _____ willingness to accept other cultures.
   d. __C__ invention of block printing.
   e. _____ ability to respond to rapid change.

Part B
For each set of statements below, write **F** for fact and **O** for opinion.

1. a. __O__ China's expansion would not have been possible without the achievements of Taizong.
   b. __F__ Taizong expanded China's borders from Korea to Afghanistan.

2. a. __F__ Taizong believed that lightening the tax burden and appointing honest officials would help stop crime.
   b. __O__ Taizong's rule was characterized by a "soft" approach to stopping crime.

3. a. __F__ Civil service examinations covered current affairs, creative writing, law, the classics, and mathematics.
   b. __O__ Civil service examinations concentrated too heavily on Chinese classics.

WORKSHEET
Chapter 9, Section 1

African Lifestyles

In this worksheet you will review Africa's major natural vegetation regions and the lifestyles of the people who inhabited them.

Part A
Only three of the four terms in each group are related in some way. Circle the term that does not belong and explain how the remaining three terms are related.

1. desert   forest   (irrigation)   savanna
Possible answer: Desert, forest, and savanna are three of Africa's major natural vegetation regions.

2. Ice Age   climate change   dry land   (oasis)
Possible answer: When the Ice Age ended, climate change brought dry land to the Sahara.

3. (cave paintings)   camel caravans   oases   traders and travelers
Possible answer: Traders and travelers crossed the Sahara in camel caravans, stopping at oases to rest and water their animals.

4. thatched straw roofs   (wooden buildings)   farming villages   compound
Possible answer: In savanna farming villages, people built houses with thatched straw roofs; several houses and a fence formed a compound.

5. poor, infertile soil   hot, wet climate   (donkeys)   tsetse fly
Possible answer: Some challenges to settlement in the forest included poor, infertile soil; a hot, wet climate; and the tsetse fly.

Part B
For each set of statements write **M** before the main idea and **S** before any statements that support or help to explain the main idea. One statement in each set is not related to the main idea. Put **X** next to this statement.

Set 1

M Towns, farms, and markets dotted the valleys formed by Africa's four great rivers.

S Farmers settled near rivers because flooding produced rich soil.

S The rivers provided fish for food and were routes for traders.

X African civilization grew along the Great Rift Valley.

Set 2

X Traders used donkeys to carry goods in the savanna.

S The people moved their homes in response to the needs of their livestock.

M One lifestyle in the savanna was that of nomadic herder.

S Nomadic herders established useful relationships with the farmers.

WORKSHEET

Chapter 9, Section 2

Early African History

Part A

Write the letter of the event from the box next to the approximate time it took place.

1. __d__ 3000 B.C.
2. __c__ 2000 B.C.
3. __h__ 800 B.C.
4. __b__ 750 B.C.
5. __g__ 630 B.C.
6. __e__ 500 B.C.
7. __a__ A.D. 350
8. __f__ A.D. 100–1000

a. Kushite power declined.
b. Kushites invaded and conquered Egypt.
c. East Africans became herders.
d. Africans began to grow rice along the Niger.
e. Forest people learned to grow yams; ironworking began in central Nigeria.
f. West Africans migrated into central and southern Africa.
g. Kushites were driven from Egypt back to their own land.
h. Ironworking became common in Egypt.

Part B

Select the word from the box that best completes each statement.

1. The kingdom of _____**Kush**_____ flourished from 750 B.C. to A.D. 350.

2. By the first century B.C., Kush was carrying on a thriving _____**iron**_____ trade with Egypt, Arabia, and India, as well as with other parts of Africa.

3. Scholars have not yet deciphered Kush _____**hieroglyphics**_____.

4. Several generations of a people all descended from the same person make up a _____**lineage**_____.

5. A lineage took care of its own members and assumed the responsibility for punishing its _____**criminals**_____.

6. Kings, queens, chiefs, and _____**elders**_____ often had to come from certain lineages.

7. Among some of the West Africans, _____**priests**_____ gained influence and power.

8. The _____**laws**_____ of the community were not written down but were known by everyone.

9. In the absence of written records, many families had their own _____**griots**_____ who memorized the family history.

laws	Kush	elders
griots	iron	criminals
priests	hieroglyphics	lineage

Name _____   Date _____

WORKSHEET
Chapter 9, Section 3

Native American Cultures

Part A
Write the letter of the phrase that best completes each statement.

1. __c__ Scientists believe that at one time exposed land formed a pathway across the Bering Strait. From this belief, scientists have concluded that
   a. the first Americans arrived in Alaska about 10,000 years ago.
   b. the first Americans were the Inuit.
   c. the first Americans were migrants from northeastern Asia.

2. __a__ Scientists learn about ancient American cultures from
   a. studying artifacts.
   b. reading books and other writings found in ancient temples.
   c. researching connections between cultures in the Americas and the Old World.

3. __c__ Scholars believe that the presence of similar inventions in the Eastern and Western hemispheres indicates that
   a. early people crossed the Pacific Ocean or Atlantic Ocean.
   b. early people brought new ideas to the Americas from Europe and Asia.
   c. people had similar ideas when they faced similar problems.

4. __b__ It is reasonable to believe that hundreds of distinct groups developed in North America over the centuries as a result of
   a. varied types of government.
   b. varied climate and geography.
   c. varied reasons for coming to the Americas.

Part B
Write a cause for each effect.

1. Our knowledge of 16th-century American cultures is sketchy.
   Possible answer: The Spanish conquerors destroyed many of the writings and buildings of the Indians they encountered.

2. Unlike many other Native American cultures, the Inuit did not develop an agricultural economy.
   Possible answer: The short growing season of their northern region did not encourage the development of agriculture.

3. The Inuit did not develop a centralized form of government.
   Possible answer: The small population of the Inuit did not require a centralized government.

4. Hundreds of distinct Native American groups developed in North America.
   Possible answer: The varied geography and climate led people in various areas to adapt differently to their environment.

WORKSHEET
Chapter 9, Section 4

In this worksheet you will
review the achievements
of the Maya civilization.

Maya Civilization

Part A

Use information from the text to complete each of the following statements about the Maya.

1. Archaeologists think that the cultures of Central America and South America
   progressed more quickly than those in the north **because**
   **Possible answer: the southern Indians had learned earlier how to
   raise corn. Their stability had allowed them more time to develop
   crafts and other skills.**

2. The Maya probably built "stelae," or large stone sculptures, **in order to**
   Possible answer: record important dates and events on them.

3. Scholars have guessed that the Maya began to abandon their cultural centers in
   the 800s **because**
   **Possible answer: too large a population, disease, crop failures,
   invasions, or revolts may have defeated the civilization.**

4. Some historians regard mathematics as the Maya's area of greatest achievement **because**
   **Possible answer: the Maya developed a highly accurate calendar and
   a number system that included the concept of zero.**

Part B

Study the explanation of the Maya number system in your text. Express each Arabic
numeral in Maya fashion.

1. 80	3. 320
2. 16	4. 11

WORKSHEET
Chapter 10, Section 1

Early Christianity

Part A
Write the letter of the term or name from the box next to its definition or identifying phrase.

a.	Palestine
b.	Saint Jerome
c.	pope
d.	Old Testament
e.	Messiah
f.	New Testament
g.	Paul
h.	Petrine Theory
i.	Saint Augustine

1. __f__ part of the Bible containing the teachings of Jesus
2. __i__ Church Father who wrote *The City of God*
3. __c__ head of the Church in the western Roman world
4. __d__ part of Bible containing the holy writings of the Jews
5. __a__ birthplace of Christianity
6. __b__ Church Father who translated the Bible from Hebrew into Latin
7. __g__ most important missionary of Christianity
8. __h__ basis of the pope's claim to the supremacy of the Church of Rome
9. __e__ Hebrew word for "anointed one"; used by Jesus' followers to refer to him

Part B
Number the events in each set in the order in which they happened.

Set 1
__3__ Paul began spreading the teachings of Christianity.

__2__ Jesus was put to death by crucifixion.

__4__ Roman emperors began widespread persecutions of Christians.

__1__ Jesus began preaching in Palestine.

Set 2
__1__ Christianity became the official religion of the eastern Roman Empire.

__3__ The Council of Nicea was called by Emperor Constantine to resolve conflict about the substance of God and Christ.

__4__ Emperor Theodosius made Christianity the official religion of the western empire.

__2__ Emperor Constantine issued the Edict of Milan, legalizing Christianity throughout the western empire.

Set 3
__3__ The Bible was translated into Latin.

__2__ Arians were barred from the western Church after refusing to accept the Nicene Creed.

__4__ Augustine finished work on his book *The City of God*.

__1__ Paul wrote letters of encouragement to persecuted believers in Christian communities.

WORKSHEET

Chapter 10, Section 2

German Tribes and the Fall of Rome

Part A

Write **T** if the statement is true and **F** if it is false. On the lines below, rewrite each false statement to make it true.

1. __F__ The Germanic peoples had no government or laws until they came into contact with the Romans.

2. __T__ German tribes attacked the Romans when the Roman Empire was plagued by internal problems.

3. __T__ German tribes felt pressured to attack Roman settlements by the Huns' attacks on German territories.

4. __F__ The year 476 is given as the date for the fall of the Roman Empire because Roman emperors had firm control of the government until that time.

5. __T__ The eastern empire kept the Greco-Roman cultural heritage alive after the collapse of the western empire.

6. __F__ Ravenna, Italy, became the capital of the eastern, or Byzantine, empire.

1. Possible answer: The Germanic peoples governed themselves through tribal assemblies and had laws based on age-old customs.

4. Possible answer: In 476 the German Odoacer became ruler of Rome without the approval of the Senate.

6. Possible answer: Constantinople became the capital of the Byzantine Empire.

Part B

Write the letter of the term or name from the box that fits the definition.

1. __b__ river that served as the southern boundary for the home of most Germanic peoples in the 4th century A.D.

2. __c__ river that served as the western boundary for the home of most Germanic peoples in the 4th century A.D.

3. __d__ German tribes from northwest Europe that invaded Britain

4. __f__ the leader of the Huns who invaded the Roman Empire in the 5th century

5. __g__ the capital of the eastern empire

6. __h__ the site of the battle in which German forces decisively defeated Roman forces

7. __e__ the German who became emperor of Rome in 476

8. __a__ the Germanic people who sacked and looted Rome in 410

a. Visigoths
b. Rhine
c. Danube
d. Anglo-Saxons
e. Odoacer
f. Attila
g. Constantinople
h. Adrianople

WORKSHEET

Chapter **10**, Section **3**

The New Civilization

In this worksheet you will review how the Christian Church emerged as the dominant force in preserving civilization in western Europe.

Part A
Complete each sentence with the explanations given in your text.

1. The number of people living in Roman cities decreased in the 4th century **because**
    Possible answer: Germanic invasions caused trade and business to decline, and the government grew unable to provide city services.

2. Farmers became serfs **because**
    Possible answer: they failed to pay their rents and were forced by Roman law to remain on the land until their debts were paid.

3. The pope and other Church officials took on such government powers as collecting taxes, supervising the police, and directing the army probably **because**
    Possible answer: Roman emperors were too weak to enforce the laws.

Part B
Fill in each blank with the letter of the item from the box that best completes each sentence.

In the years during and after the decline of the Roman Empire, followers of the Christian Church expressed their faith and served the Church in many different ways. Persons known as __f__ traveled to distant lands to convert others to Christianity. The Arian Christian __k__ won converts among the Gothic peoples, while __h__ convinced Celtic people in Ireland to become Christians. The Roman monk __d__ journeyed to England where his talks with the king of Kent led to the king's conversion.

Some religious people preferred to live alone. Known as __a__, people such as __g__ believed that by fasting and depriving themselves of human company and everyday comforts, they could become better people. A more common way for religious people to express their faith was to live in communities separate from the world. These places were known as *convents* if __i__ lived in them and *monasteries* if __b__ lived there. Convents and monasteries had strict rules about praying and working. Some monasteries followed rules drawn up by __e__, who set up a monastery in Italy in 520. One important way monasteries served the community was by copying and preserving manuscripts. Monasteries also maintained historical records. __j__, for example, wrote __c__ recounting 200 years of the early history of England.

a. hermits
b. monks
c. chronicles
d. Augustine
e. Saint Benedict
f. missionaries
g. Saint Simeon Stylites
h. Saint Patrick
i. nuns
j. Saint Bede
k. Ulfilas

WORKSHEET
Chapter 10, Section 4

In this worksheet you will review the history of the Frankish Empire.

Frankish Rule in Europe

Part A
Underline the word *before* or *after* in each sentence to make the statement correct.

1. Clovis attacked his Arian neighbors and took their lands (before/after) Charles Martel took control of the Frankish kingdom.

2. The office of Mayor of the Palace became a powerful position (before/after) the reign of the Do-Nothing Kings ended.

3. Aix-la-Chapelle became the capital of the Frankish Empire (before/after) Charlemagne inherited the throne.

4. The Franks won the battle of Tours (before/after) the death of Charlemagne.

5. The lands of the Franks were expanded to become an empire (before/after) the death of Charlemagne.

6. The pope crowned Charlemagne Emperor of the Romans (before/after) the Donation of Pepin.

Part B
Each item below represents an achievement of the reign of Charlemagne. For each item, write two or three sentences that explain or provide details of that achievement.

1. encouragement of education
   Example: Charlemagne urged priests to improve their own educations. He supported Church and monastery schools and sponsored a refinement of the system of handwriting. He also encouraged a rebirth of learning.

   _____

   _____

   _____

2. extension of the power of the Christian Church
   Example: Priests who accompanied Charlemagne converted non-Christian conquered peoples to Christianity. Charlemagne allowed the pope to crown him emperor.

   _____

   _____

   _____

   _____

WORKSHEET
Chapter 11, Section 1

In this worksheet you will review the decline of the Carolingian empire and the rise of feudalism.

The Rise of Feudalism

Part A
Only three of the four items in each group are related in some way. Circle the item that does not belong and explain how the remaining three items are related.

1. Carolingian empire   Treaty of Verdun   three kingdoms   (Muslims)
   Possible answer: The Treaty of Verdun, which divided the Carolingian empire into three kingdoms, led to the empire's decline.

2. villeins   serfs   peasants   (priests)
   Possible answer: Villeins, serfs, and peasants all worked the land in medieval society.

3. Vikings   Normans   Normandy   (Muslims)
   Possible answer: Vikings, known as Normans, were invited to settle in the region that became known as Normandy.

4. feudalism   (centralized government)   land ownership   loyalty
   Possible answer: Feudalism was a system of government based on land ownership and loyalty.

5. fief   feud   (merchants)   land
   Possible answer: The land granted by the lord to his vassals was called a fief or a feud.

Part B
The centralized economic and political systems of the Carolingian empire were gradually replaced by the feudal system, in which economic and political agreements took place on a local scale. The triangle shows how society was organized under feudalism. Place these terms on the correct level of the triangle: vassals, serfs. Describe the feudal responsibilities of the people at each level of society.

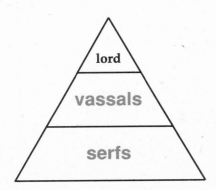

Responsibilities

Possible answer: (lord) grant fiefs to vassals; protect vassals; provide justice

(vassals) serve in army; pay taxes; give shelter, entertainment, and food to lord

(serfs) do menial work for vassals or lords

WORKSHEET
Chapter 11, Section 2

In this worksheet you will review living conditions in a medieval castle.

A Medieval Castle

Read the clues below and complete the crossword puzzle using the terms in the box.

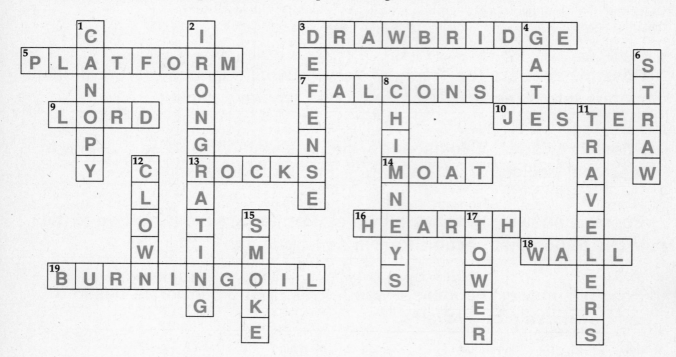

Across
3. movable plank that controlled entrance to a castle
5. supportive structure of medieval beds
7. birds that might be found in sleeping rooms
9. castle owner
10. one type of castle entertainer
13. objects thrown to repel enemy attacks on castle
14. water barrier around castle
16. location of a castle's fire
18. high, thick barrier around a castle
19. liquid often poured on the enemy by a castle's defenders (two words)

Down
1. structure above a castle bed
2. heavy item dropped to close a drawbridge gate (two words)
3. one purpose of a castle
4. structure connected to a drawbridge
6. covering for the castle floor
8. 14th-century fireplace additions
11. bearers of news from outside the castle
12. one type of castle entertainer
15. asphyxiating fumes in castle rooms before invention of chimneys
17. shelter during a castle siege

falcons	clown	gate	moat
chimneys	canopy	smoke	travelers
defense	straw	platform	wall
burning oil	iron grating	drawbridge	tower
rocks	hearth	jester	lord

WORKSHEET
Chapter 11, Section 3

The Feudal Church

In this worksheet you will review the ways in which the Church unified Europe during the Middle Ages.

Part A
Write **C** next to each phrase that correctly completes the unfinished sentence. (Each incomplete sentence may have more than one correct ending.)

1. The papacy's reliance on the protection of the German kings in the 10th century resulted in

    _____ the election of German popes.

    __C__ defense of the papacy against feudal abuses and unruly nobles.

    __C__ German interference in Church matters.

    __C__ a great religious reform movement begun by the monks at Cluny.

2. The 11th-century religious reform movement

    _____ created the papacy.

    __C__ objected to the sale of positions in the Church.

    __C__ created the College of Cardinals.

    __C__ was begun by the monks of Cluny.

3. Crusades were formed

    __C__ to support the Byzantine emperor against the Turks.

    __C__ to win Christians the right to visit Jerusalem.

    _____ to restore the Holy Roman Empire.

    __C__ following Pope Urban's promise of forgiveness and fiefs for crusaders.

Part B
Write the letter of the term from the box next to its definition or identifying phrase.

1. __f__ exclusion of a Church member from the Church

2. __c__ the reenactment of the Last Supper

3. __g__ passage from childhood to adulthood in the Church

4. __a__ beliefs contrary to Church doctrine

5. __d__ the sacrament of marriage

6. __e__ sacrament administered to the dying

7. __i__ atonement for sins after confession

8. __h__ the rite through which one becomes a Christian in the Church

9. __b__ sacrament conferring priesthood

a. heresy
b. holy orders
c. the Holy Eucharist
d. matrimony
e. extreme unction
f. excommunication
g. confirmation
h. baptism
i. penance

WORKSHEET

Chapter 11, Section 4

Medieval Towns and Guilds

In this worksheet you will review the growth of towns and guilds in medieval Europe.

Part A

For each of the following pairs of words, write a sentence that clearly explains the relationship between the two.

1. barter/money

Possible answer: The use of money instead of barter made it easier for merchants to develop businesses.

2. fairs/banking

Possible answer: Banking developed from the practice of exchanging foreign coins for local currency at trade fairs.

3. Black Death/urban decline

Possible answer: The Black Death caused urban decline—as shown by the cities' sharp drop in population, education, and commerce.

Part B

Read the paragraph about the guilds and answer the questions that follow.

Free enterprise as we know it today was unknown to medieval people. The owner of each shop was required to be a member of the guild and to follow strict guidelines. Prices were fixed according to the medieval concept of the "just price," guaranteeing the worker a fair wage for his labor. A guild member faced regulations about the type and quality of raw materials to be used, the methods by which he could make his product, and even the hours he could work. The guild made sure that only its members carried on trade within specific areas. Any man who was not a member of a specific guild was forbidden to work in the craft of that guild. Modern business competition with its emphasis on producing better goods at lower prices simply did not exist.

1. Find the definition of monopoly in the text. According to the paragraph, in what ways did guilds establish monopolies?

Possible answer: Guild rules were designed to establish and maintain exclusive control over a commodity's production.

2. What guild regulations might an American small businessperson find most objectionable?

Possible answer: regulations governing prices, hours, methods of production, and entry into business

3. What is the main idea of the paragraph?

Possible answer: Guilds did not operate in a way that promoted free enterprise.

WORKSHEET

Chapter 11, Section 5

Literature and Learning

Part A

Explain in one or two sentences the changes that took place in medieval Europe in each of the following areas.

1. education

   Possible answer: Between 600 and 1100 only Church schools existed. After 1150 secular universities were established to train people for law or government service.

2. spoken language

   Possible answer: Latin remained the language of the Church and educated people. However, Latin-based languages, which became the popularly spoken tongues, were evolving.

3. written language and literature

   Possible answer: Before the 8th century, Latin was the language used in literature. From the 8th century on, native literature appeared. Both Chaucer and Dante used local dialects for their literary works.

Part B

For each set of statements below, write **M** before the main idea and **S** before statements that support or help explain the main idea. One statement in each set is not related to the main idea; write **X** next to this statement.

1. __M__ During the lifetime of Saint Thomas Aquinas, a controversy developed among scholars about the true source of knowledge.

   __S__ Ancient Greek writings influenced many scholars to insist on reason as a source of knowledge.

   __S__ Thomas Aquinas disagreed with the Greek view that reason is the source of all knowledge.

   __X__ Thomas Aquinas was a Dominican lecturer, scholar, and writer.

   __S__ Church leaders generally held that faith is the source of knowledge.

2. __X__ Roger Bacon was imprisoned for his ideas.

   __S__ Bacon disagreed with Thomas Aquinas as to the sources of knowledge.

   __M__ Roger Bacon was an English monk who made significant contributions to knowledge.

   __S__ Bacon believed that continued experimentation could lead to the truth.

   __S__ Bacon predicted the invention of machinery that would free man from the need for labor.

WORKSHEET
Chapter 12, Section 1

The Growth of Nations

Part A

Each pair of sentences below contains one factual statement and one statement of opinion. Write **F** for the fact and **O** for the opinion.

1. a. __O__ All the people within a nation are loyal to and proud of their national group.

   b. __F__ A nation is a group of people occupying the same country, living under the same government, and usually speaking the same language.

2. a. __F__ The bourgeoisie occupied a social status lower than that of the nobles who owned land but higher than that of the peasants who farmed the nobles' land.

   b. __O__ The bourgeoisie was the most important class of the late medieval period.

3. a. __F__ In the late medieval period, trade within and between states expanded.

   b. __O__ Since the expansion of trade increased a state's wealth, kings should have provided free protection for commerce.

4. a. __O__ Strong kings were a blessing for all the people of Europe.

   b. __F__ The development of strong national governments followed the pattern of freeing the monarch from the old feudal lord-vassal patterns.

Part B

Each pair of sentences establishes a relationship of cause and effect. Identify which sentence states the cause and which states the effect by writing **C** for cause and **E** for effect.

1. a. __E__ The bourgeoisie grew richer and more influential than some of the noble class.

   b. __C__ During the late medieval period, trade between nearby and more distant regions grew rapidly.

2. a. __C__ Feudal nobles controlled the highways that passed through their fiefs.

   b. __E__ Citizens became unhappy with the high tolls charged for the use of roads.

3. a. __E__ Monarchs could free themselves from the feudal system by paying their own soldiers to take the place of the armies of feudal lords.

   b. __C__ The monarchs found new sources of income by taxing the bourgeoisie.

4. a. __E__ The systems and applications of law became more uniform.

   b. __C__ Monarchs forced local nobles to turn over their courts to the king.

WORKSHEET
Chapter 12, Section 2

Toward an English Nation

In this worksheet you will
review England's change
from a medieval kingdom
into a national state.

Part A
Write **T** if the statement is true and **F** if it is false. On the lines below, rewrite each
false statement to make it true.

1. **T** William the Conqueror gained the name "Conqueror" because he
defeated Harold at the battle of Hastings in 1066.

2. **F** The rule of the Tudor kings began with the ascendancy of Henry II to the
English throne.

3. **F** Among the important reforms made by Henry II was the establishment of
Parliament as a legislative body.

4. **T** Thomas à Becket, archbishop of Canterbury, may have been murdered by
Henry II's knights because he had quarreled with Henry.

5. **F** The Magna Carta, developed by King John's nobles, increased the power
of the English monarchy.

6. **T** Parliament began to refuse to grant money to a ruler until a ruler
corrected wrongs, or addressed grievances.

**2. Possible answer: The rule of the Plantagenet kings began with the
ascendancy of Henry II to the English throne.**

**3. Possible answer: Among the important reforms made by Henry II
were the establishment of common law, circuit courts, and the
jury system.**

**5. Possible answer: The Magna Carta, developed by King John's nobles,
limited John's power and protected the nobles' feudal rights.**

Part B
Write the letter of each event at its approximate place on the time line.

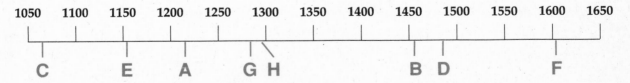

| 1050 | 1100 | 1150 | 1200 | 1250 | 1300 | 1350 | 1400 | 1450 | 1500 | 1550 | 1600 | 1650 |

C   E   A   G H   B   D   F

A. King John agrees to the Magna Carta.
B. The Wars of the Roses begin.
C. William defeats Harold in the battle of Hastings.
D. Henry Tudor (Henry VII) wins the throne.
E. Henry II's reign begins.
F. The Tudor dynasty ends.
G. Edward I conquers Wales.
H. Edward I calls together the Model Parliament.

WORKSHEET
Chapter 12, Section 3

In this worksheet you will review the growth of France as a national state.

Nation-Building in France

Part A
Number the events in the order in which they happened.

__2__ The centralized government collapsed.

__4__ Louis VI gained full control of royal lands.

__1__ Charlemagne centralized the Frankish government.

__3__ Hugh Capet was elected king of France by the nobles.

__6__ Edward III claimed the French throne.

__7__ Joan of Arc led the French army to victory at Orleans.

__5__ Louis IX set up a system of royal courts.

__8__ The Hundred Years' War ended.

Part B
Write **C** next to each phrase that correctly completes the unfinished sentence. (Each incomplete sentence may have more than one correct ending.)

1. The Capetian kings strengthened the French government by

   __C__ putting down the barons who threatened their power.

   _____ encouraging private wars and trial by combat.

   __C__ winning Normandy, Anjou, and other English holdings.

   __C__ setting up a system of royal courts.

   _____ developing a strong parliament.

2. The Hundred Years' War resulted from

   __C__ a dynastic quarrel between France and England.

   __C__ English possession of lands in France.

   _____ the last Capetian king leaving a war-loving young son to reign.

   __C__ English and French conflict over the control of Flanders.

   _____ France's desire to have William the Conqueror as its king.

3. Joan of Arc was successful in rallying the French during the Hundred Years' War because

   _____ she was the long-lost daughter of the French king.

   __C__ the French soldiers accepted her as a heaven-sent leader.

   _____ the French soldiers were exhausted from the long seige of Orleans.

   __C__ she gave the French soldiers a nearly mystical confidence in themselves.

   _____ she bewitched the English soldiers.

WORKSHEET

Chapter 12, Section 4

The Growth of National States

Part A
Number the events in each set in the order in which they happened.

Set 1

__1__ The Moors conquered the kingdom of the Visigoths on the Iberian peninsula.

__4__ Ferdinand of Aragon married Isabella of Castile.

__5__ Ferdinand and Isabella conquered Moorish Granada and united Spain.

__3__ Portugal became an independent kingdom.

__2__ Christians began a crusade to regain Spain for Christendom.

Set 2

__1__ German kings began to bring their country under a strong central government.

__3__ Otto the Great was crowned emperor by the pope, effectively beginning the Holy Roman Empire.

__4__ Frederick Barbarossa warred against the Italian city-states.

__2__ Henry the Fowler forced his nobles to pledge their loyalty to him.

__5__ Both Italy and Germany were unified.

Set 3

__2__ Polish tribes were united under one king; the Czechs of Bohemia and Moravia were joined under the king of Bohemia.

__5__ Norway broke away from Denmark.

__4__ Sweden revolted and broke away from the Danish empire.

__1__ Magyar tribes formed the kingdom of Hungary.

__3__ Danish queen Margaret I forged Denmark, Norway, and Sweden into an empire.

Part B
Use information from your text to complete each of the following sentences.

1. The __Iberian peninsula__ is the modern-day home of Spain and Portugal.

2. The breakup of the kingdom of the _____ __Moors__ _____ inspired Christians to regain Spain for Christendom.

3. The reconquest of Spain by the Christians is known as the _____ __Reconquista__ _____.

4. Since Ferdinand and Isabella believed that national unity required religious conformity, they revived the _____ __Inquisition__ _____, a medieval procedure for punishing heretics, and expelled the _____ __Jews__ _____ from Spain.

5. _____ __Otto the Great__ _____ was the first ruler of the Holy Roman Empire.

WORKSHEET

Chapter 13, Section 1

The Eastern Empire

In this worksheet you will review important people and events of the Eastern Empire.

Part A

Select the name from the box that best completes each statement. Some names may be used more than once. Some names may not be used.

1. In his attempt to restore a united Roman Empire, **Justinian** succeeded only in recovering parts of the West from the Germanic tribes.

2. **Constantine** established an eastern capital at Byzantium.

3. **Leo III** drove the Arabs out of Constantinople.

4. The collection of Roman law put together by **Justinian** became the law of the land for as long as the Eastern Empire lasted.

5. **Theodora** set the pattern for a Byzantine empress' active role in government.

| Constantine | Anna Comnena | Justinian | Leo III | Theodora |

Part B

For each set of statements below, write **M** before the main idea and **S** before any statements that support or help to explain the main idea. One statement in each set is not related to the main idea; write **X** next to this statement.

Set 1

S The civilization that ruled the eastern Mediterranean for more than a millenium was Roman in foundation, law, and heritage.

S The Byzantine population was mostly Greek.

X The site of ancient Byzantium was a strategic location at the center of north-south sea lanes and east-west caravan routes.

S The Byzantine emperor adopted the elaborate court etiquette and lavish state ceremonies that were associated with the Persian monarch.

M Byzantine society was shaped by Roman, Greek, and Persian cultures.

Set 2

X The Byzantines were Christians who built their culture on the Greek plan but nevertheless called themselves Romans.

M The Byzantine emperor ruled over both church and state.

S The clearly defined relationship between the emperor and the patriarch prevented friction between church and state.

S The relationship between the Byzantine emperor and the Orthodox Church patriarch eliminated the question of who was the supreme power.

S The Byzantine emperor appointed the patriarch of the Orthodox church, who ran church affairs in the same way that the emperor's ministers handled the details of the civil government.

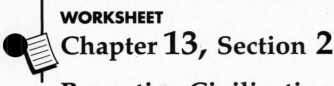

WORKSHEET
Chapter 13, Section 2

Byzantine Civilization

In this worksheet you will examine the civilization of the Byzantine Empire.

Part A
Complete each statement with the explanations given in your text.

1. The Byzantines were able to build a strong empire **because**
   Possible answer: they had a centralized government with a well-trained bureaucracy, an efficient army and navy, a strong economy, and an effective religious leadership in the Orthodox Church.

2. Periods of conflict and civil war followed the deaths of many of the emperors **because**
   Possible answer: there was no clear, legal system of succession.

3. Constantinople became the world's greatest center of trade partly **because**
   Possible answer: it was located at the crossroads of Europe and Asia.

4. The Byzantine government played an active part in controlling industry, wages, prices, and the quality of exports **because**
   Possible answer: economic activity was important to the health of the empire.

5. Byzantine architecture and decorative art are more highly admired than Byzantine scholarship **because**
   Possible answer: most scholarship, with the exception of history and theology, was dull and unoriginal, while Byzantine architecture and art were magnificent.

Part B
The Byzantine government served as a watchdog for its economy. Imperial inspectors checked the quality of goods for export. Explain how this practice helped the Byzantine economy.
Possible answer: Imperial inspectors ensured that the goods produced in the Byzantine Empire and sent to other parts of the world were of high quality. The Byzantine reputation for high-quality goods increased the demand for the goods and brought prosperity to the empire.

WORKSHEET

Chapter 13, Section 3

Early Russia

In this worksheet you
will locate places that
were important to the
establishment of
Kievan Russia.

Part A

Write the letter from the map for the location of each place listed below. Draw an
arrow on the map to show the direction from which the Slavs migrated to eastern
Europe and from which the Mongols later invaded Russia.

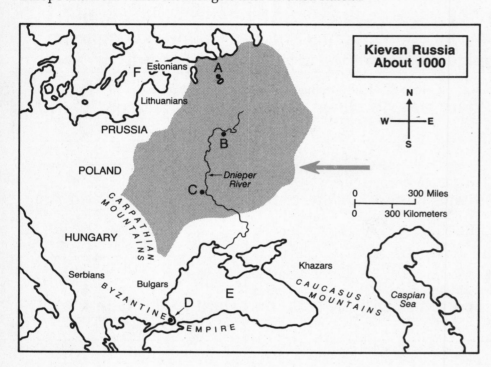

1. __D__ Constantinople
2. __B__ Smolensk
3. __A__ Novgorod
4. __C__ Kiev
5. __F__ Baltic Sea
6. __E__ Black Sea

Part B

Use the map to answer the following questions.

1. What does the shaded area on the map represent?
   Kievan Russia

2. Why was the conquest of the Turkish people along the Black Sea a strategic
   victory for the rulers of Kiev?
   **Possible answer: It enabled Kiev to control the water route to
   Constantinople through the Black Sea.**

3. Why do you think the Black Sea might have been more important to the Kievan
   state than the Baltic Sea?
   **Possible answer: The Black Sea provided access to the heavily
   populated Mediterranean states. In addition, the Baltic Sea probably
   was frozen for much of the year.**

WORKSHEET
Chapter 13, Section 4

Mongol and Russian Rule

Part A
Write the letter of the correct description from the box beside each name.

1. __c__ Alexander Nevsky
2. __b__ Daniel
3. __a__ Ivan the Great
4. __e__ Ivan the Terrible
5. __d__ Batu
6. __f__ Genghis Khan

a. He ended Mongol rule in Russia and took the title of tsar.
b. He built up Moscow's strength and improved trade on the Volga River.
c. He defeated a Swedish army on the Neva River.
d. He captured Kiev and other Russian states, forcing the Russians into subservience to the Mongols.
e. He led the Russians in their conquest of Kazar, effectively ending the Mongol threat to Europe.
f. He led the Mongolian tribes in their invasions of China, Persia, and Russia.

Part B
Present one or two specific facts from your text to support each statement.

1. The Mongols halted the development of Russia by 150 to 200 years.
   Possible answer: The Russian economy was devastated by the large tribute the Russians had to pay their conquerors. The Mongols kept the Russians isolated from Western Christendom.

2. The Mongols did little to add to Russian civilization.
   Possible answer: The Mongols contributed little to Russia except for a postal system and a census. As Muslims in a Christian land, the Mongols were alien to Russian culture.

3. During the Mongol rule, Moscow replaced Kiev as the center of Russia.
   Possible answer: The princes of Moscow built up the city's strength without appearing to threaten Mongol rule. The Mongols gave the Moscow princes precedence over other Russian rulers.

4. Although Ivan the Great and Ivan the Terrible unified and strengthened Russia, they did so at the expense of the Russian people.
   Possible answer: Ivan the Great slowly acquired one small state after another until he ruled most of the Russian people; towns that had been self-governing lost their freedom. Ivan the Terrible brought the nomadic tribes of the eastern steppes under Russian rule, but heavier taxes forced free Russian peasants into serfdom.

WORKSHEET
Chapter 14, Section 1

In this worksheet you will review the development of Islam.

Muhammad and Islam

Part A
Complete each statement with the explanations given in your text.

1. In the 6th and 7th centuries A.D., trade routes shifted to the south near the Red Sea and Persian Gulf coasts **because**
   Possible answer: constant warfare between Persians and Byzantines interrupted commerce in the eastern Mediterranean.

2. Muhammad fled Mecca in 622 **because**
   Possible answer: the wealthy merchants who dominated Mecca began to persecute him.

3. There was little racism in the Muslim world **because**
   Possible answer: Muhammad taught that every believer is equal to every other believer.

4. No organized or privileged priesthood has ever existed in Islam **because**
   Possible answer: Islam teaches that no human can intervene between God and another person.

5. As many peoples throughout the Middle East converted to Islam, the use of Arabic spread **because**
   Possible answer: only the Arabic words of the Koran could be used for the formal prayers of worship.

Part B
Write a brief definition of each term or name as it relates to Islam.

1. Hijra
   Possible answer: Muhammad's flight from Mecca; the beginning of the Muslim calendar

2. Koran
   Possible answer: the Muslim holy book; the record of God's revelations to Muhammad

4. Five Pillars
   Possible answer: the five duties of a good Muslim taught in the Koran

WORKSHEET
Chapter 14, Section 2

The Rise of Islam

In this worksheet you
will review the spread
of Islam.

Part A
Fill in the blanks with the terms or names from the box that best complete the
sentences.

Berbers
jihad
Constantinople
Kabul
sharia
Moors
Damascus

1. People of mixed Arab and Berber ancestry who gave their name to a
    civilization in Spain were called the _____**Moors**_____.

2. The part of the Koran that states the law of Islam is called the
    _____**sharia**_____.

3. The Byzantine capital, _____**Constantinople**_____, was attacked by the Arabs
    many times but never taken by them.

4. The Arab governor of Syria declared himself caliph and made
    _____**Damascus**_____ his capital.

5. The word _____**jihad**_____ means "struggle" in Arabic but
    is usually translated as "holy war."

6. The _____**Berbers**_____ were a nomadic tribal people of northwest
    Africa who were conquered and converted to Islam under the Umayyad armies.

7. The capital of modern Afghanistan, _____**Kabul**_____, was conquered
    by the Arab armies in the first century of Islam.

Part B
For each statement below, write two or three sentences that support or provide
details for that statement.

1. The early spread of Islam was motivated partly by a population explosion in the
    trading centers of the Arabian peninsula.
    **Possible answer: The prosperity of the caravan trade and the Meccan
    markets created a population explosion. The Arabian deserts could
    not support large numbers of people, and new areas were needed
    for settlement.**

2. The weaknesses of neighboring states—the Byzantine and Persian empires—
    contributed to the early success of Arab armies.
    **Possible answer: Byzantines and Persians had been fighting each
    other for centuries. Tired of warfare and heavy taxes, the conquered
    peoples in these two empires barely resisted—and even welcomed—
    the Arabs.**

WORKSHEET

Chapter 14, Section 3

Divisions Within Islam

Part A

For each set of statements below, write **M** before the main idea and **S** before any statements that support or help to explain the main idea. One statement in each set is not related to the main idea; write **X** next to this statement.

Set 1

S   Ali's followers formed the Shiite sect and supported Hussein in his attempt to regain the caliphate.

X   Moving the capital to Baghdad lessened the empire's control over North Africa and Spain.

S   The Umayyads were not accepted as caliphs of Islam by the Shiites.

S   The Shiites found inspiration in Hussein's martyrdom at Karbala and have made his grave there a pilgrimage shrine.

M   The Shiite Muslims, a minority sect of Islam, formed as a result of a series of events that occurred during the early years of the Islamic Empire.

Set 2

X   The Fatimids, the Druse, the Alawi, and the Assassins were Shiites who split into separate groups.

S   In 750 a revolution that had been carefully planned by the Abbasids took place.

M   The Abbasids replaced the Umayyads as rulers of Islam.

S   The non-Arab Muslims who had been treated poorly by their Arab conquerors were dissatisfied with Umayyad rule.

S   The Abbasids promised that all Muslims would be treated equally.

Part B

Write the word from the box that best completes each statement.

| Shiites |
| Baghdad |
| Harun al-Rashid |
| Sunnis |
| Umayyad |
| Abbasid |

1. **Harun al-Rashid** and Charlemagne promoted peace between their empires.

2. The Abbasids built a new capital, **Baghdad**, on the banks of the Tigris River.

3. Women lost the freedom to participate in much of society under the later **Abbasid** rulers.

4. The **Sunnis** accepted the Umayyad caliphs as rulers of the Muslim community.

5. Through 12 generations, the **Shiites** secretly supported Ali's descendants as the rightful rulers of Islam.

6. The **Umayyad** rulers refused to grant full citizenship rights to non-Arab Muslims.

WORKSHEET
Chapter 14, Section 4

The Turks and the Mongols

In this worksheet you
will review events in
the Turkish and Mongol
domination of the Islamic
Empire.

Part A
Number the events in the order in which they happened.

__4__ The Latin Christians established several Crusader States in Syria
and Palestine.

__8__ The Ottoman Turks conquered and reunited the Muslim lands of the
Middle East.

__2__ The Seljuk Turks invaded Baghdad.

__5__ Saladin attacked the Crusader States, recaptured Jerusalem, and provoked
the launching of the Third Crusade.

__1__ Turkish nomads from Central Asia migrated into Abbasid Persia.

__6__ The Mongol Hulagu sacked and burned Baghdad.

__3__ The Seljuk armies defeated the Greeks at the battle of Manzikert.

__7__ The Ottoman Turks captured Constantinople.

Part B
Only three of the four items in each group are related in some way. Circle the item
that does not belong and explain how the remaining three items are related.

1. Seljuk Turks   Baghdad   Abbasids   (Istanbul)

   **Possible answer: The Seljuk Turks invaded Baghdad in 1055,
   but instead of deposing the Abbasid rulers, the Turks became
   their patrons.**

2. (Constantinople)   Seljuks   Saladin   Islam

   **Possible answer: Saladin waited to take the throne of Islam until the
   Seljuks began to quarrel among themselves.**

3. Kings' Crusade   (Genghis Khan)   Saladin   Richard the Lion-Hearted

   **Possible answer: Richard the Lion-Hearted of England led Christian
   troops against Saladin in the Kings' Crusade.**

4. (Saladin)   Ottoman Turks   Constantinople   Istanbul

   **Possible answer: In 1453 the Ottoman Turks captured Constantinople
   and changed the city's name to Istanbul.**

WORKSHEET

Chapter 14, Section 5

In this worksheet you
will review the Muslim
invasion of India.

The Muslims Overpower India

Part A
In the blank before each item below, write the letter from the time line that matches
the date of the item.

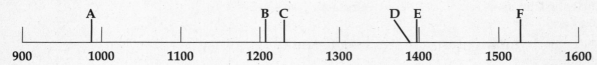

1. __E__ Tamerlane sacked India and gutted Delhi.

2. __B__ The Turks established the Delhi Sultanate.

3. __C__ The Tower of Kutb Minar was built.

4. __F__ The Mughals invaded India.

5. __A__ Mahmud of Ghazni made his first raid in India.

6. __D__ Firuz Shah Tughlak died, and civil war began in India.

Part B
Write **C** next to each phrase that correctly completes the unfinished sentence.
(Each incomplete sentence may have more than one correct ending.)

1. The Indians'

   _____ commanders were well organized
   and efficient.

   __C__ warrior caste was the only caste used
   for defense.

   __C__ military tactics were out of date.

   _____ use of elephants in battle successfully
   blocked the advance of the enemy.

2. Muslim warrior tribes

   __C__ set themselves up as kings and princes
   in India.

   _____ admired the Hindu caste system.

   __C__ were strict monotheists.

   __C__ looted Indian cities.

3. Tamerlane

   __C__ wreaked havoc in India that was never
   repaired.

   __C__ massacred everyone in Delhi except
   artisans and women.

   _____ made India his final conquest.

   __C__ kept both his Muslim and non-Muslim
   neighbors weak.

4. The Muslims

   _____ were overwhelmed by the Hindus' social
   cohesiveness and political unity.

   _____ were absorbed into the Hindu culture.

   __C__ were contemptuous of Hindu customs.

   __C__ sometimes used violence to force the
   Hindus to embrace Islam.

WORKSHEET
Chapter 15, Section 1

In this worksheet you will review some aspects of life in the Islamic Empire.

The Islamic Empire

Part A
Write a cause for each effect.

1. Arabic became the vernacular throughout the Middle East and North Africa.
   Possible answer: Converts to Islam were required to read the Koran and pray in Arabic.

2. Occasionally, kings gave up their rule after performing the Hajj.
   Possible answer: The Hajj often inspired Muslims to reform their lives.

3. The Hajj became an enormous school for the pilgrims.
   Possible answer: In Mecca, Muslims exchanged ideas with people from other areas of the world.

4. In general, Muslims were a literate people.
   Possible answer: Schools were set up at neighborhood mosques so even poor children could read and memorize the Koran.

5. Persian and Byzantine culture did not disappear upon conquest by the Arab armies.
   Possible answer: The Arabs appreciated the cultures they encountered and did much to preserve them.

Part B
Support each statement with examples from your text.

1. Most of the major cities of the Islamic Empire specialized in the manufacture of particular products.
   Example: Baghdad became known for glassware, jewelry, silks; Cordova for leathers; Damascus for steel and damask.

2. People in the cities of the Islamic Empire enjoyed a standard of living higher than that of the Europeans of the same time period.
   Example: Cities in the Islamic Empire had colleges, libraries, efficient drainage systems, restaurants, and public baths. Homes had modern conveniences.

WORKSHEET

Chapter 15, Section 2

The Economy of the Islamic Empire

Part A
Complete each statement with the explanations given in your text.

1. Muslim joint-stock ventures encouraged the growth of business **because**
   Possible answer: they encouraged large-scale trading expeditions by allowing several persons to pool their money.

2. The spread of Islam to Southeast Asia suffered a major setback in 1571 **because**
   Possible answer: in that year the Spanish introduced Christianity to the Filipinos.

3. Ibn Batuta's *Travels* may be regarded as an important historical source **because**
   Possible answer: it describes West Africa in the 1300s.

4. Ibn Batuta was able to find work wherever he went during his 75,000-mile journey **because**
   Possible answer: as a judge, he could interpret Islamic law in most of the places he visited.

5. During the 1300s Muslim merchants and navigators were important in spreading Islam **because**
   Possible answer: they carried their religion, along with their goods, to parts of East and West Africa, China, and Southeast Asia.

Part B
Write **C** next to each phrase that correctly completes the unfinished sentence.
(Each incomplete sentence may have more than one cor)rect ending.

1. Practices that encouraged the growth of trade in the Islamic Empire included

   C   the absence of tariffs or import duties.

   _____   reliance on barter.

   C   the formation of joint-stock ventures.

   C   the development of a banking system.

2. Muslim sailors

   C   sailed to India and China hundreds of years before Western Europeans.

   C   used the compass and the astrolabe.

   _____   were unable to help the advance of Islam in Indonesia.

   _____   avoided the Persian Gulf and the Indian Ocean.

WORKSHEET

Chapter 15, Section 3

Muslim Science and Arts

In this worksheet you will review the contributions of Islamic civilization in the fields of science and literature.

Part A
Only three of the four items in each set are related in some way. Circle the one that does not belong and explain how the remaining three items are related.

1. Averroes   Maimonides   Aristotle   (Avicenna)

   Possible answer: Both Maimonides and Averroes were philosophers who interpreted the ideas of Aristotle for the Islamic world.

2. minarets   horseshoe arch   (Ionic columns)   arcade

   Possible answer: A distinct Muslim style of architecture included the use of minarets, the horseshoe arch, and the arcade.

3. Cordova   Baghdad   Damascus   (Ibn Khaldun)

   Possible answer: Damascus, Baghdad, and Cordova were major Islamic cities with beautiful examples of Muslim architecture.

4. arabesques   geometric patterns   floral designs   (portraits)

   Possible answer: Islamic artists executed intricate geometric patterns, floral designs, and vinelike motifs known as arabesques.

Part B
Give at least one example of a Muslim achievement in each of the following areas.

1. chemistry
   Possible answer: Alchemists invented various methods of distillation and crystallization and discovered new substances.

2. optics
   Possible answer: Al-Hazen challenged the Greek view that the eye sends rays to the object it sees.

3. astronomy
   Possible answer: Arabs made more accurate measurements of the length of the solar year, calculated eclipses, and made atlases of the night sky.

4. literature
   Possible answer: The poetry of Omar Khayyam, who wrote the *Rubaiyat*, is well-known. The *Arabian Nights* includes many Persian and Indian stories.

WORKSHEET

Chapter 15, Section 4

Islam and West Africa

Part A
Place the letter of the effect from the box next to its cause.

1. __c__ existence of large gold deposits in West Africa

2. __d__ 13th-century conversion of mansas to Islam

3. __b__ Mansa Musa's pilgrimage to Mecca in 1324

4. __a__ Mansa Musa's attempt to convert people to Islam by force

> **a.** the threat of a strike by Mali miners
> **b.** world notice of the wealth of Mali
> **c.** the development of caravan trade routes across the Sahara
> **d.** transformation of Mali into the center of Islamic culture in West Africa

Part B
Describe Mali life in the 14th century in each of the following areas.

1. role of women
   Possible answer: Women in Mali, unlike their counterparts in other Muslim countries, were not kept out of public sight, nor were they required to obey their husbands.

2. laws and legal code
   Possible answer: At least some aspects of Islamic law were incorporated into the Mali system of government. The people had a strong sense of justice, wrongdoers were swiftly punished, and both city and countryside were fairly safe.

3. scholarship and education
   Possible answer: Mali was the center of Islamic learning in West Africa. Scholars from all over the Muslim world came to study Arabic manuscripts in the Timbuktu library.

© Scott, Foresman and Company

WORKSHEET

Chapter 16, Section 1

Song Achievements

In this worksheet you
will review the major
achievements of the
Song dynasty.

Part A
Use information from your text to complete the chart.

Advances of the Song Era

Category	Advances	Significance
Farming	**moldboard, strains of rice from Southeast Asia**	led to increased crop production and growth in population and trade
Industry	tools for spinning and weaving	**increased silk and cotton production**
	movable type	advanced printing and scholarship
Trade	**abacus**	allowed merchants to conduct transactions more quickly
	magnetic compass, ships propelled by paddle wheels	**expanded sea trade**

Part B
Define each theme and explain how it is illustrated by Song China.

1. dynastic cycle

definition:
the cyclical rise and fall of dynasties

in Song China:
Example: The first Song emperors were strong rulers who united China. Eventually, internal corruption weakened Song rule, and the Jin, a Manchurian group of nomads, were able to force the Song to retreat to southern China.

2. continuity of Chinese culture

definition:
assimilation of other cultures into the mainstream Chinese

in Song China:
Example: Despite the conquest of northern China by the Jin, Chinese culture continued to predominate in the region, and many Jin leaders adopted the Chinese culture.

WORKSHEET

Chapter 16, Section 2

In this worksheet you will support generalizations about life and values in the Song era.

Life and Values in Song China

For each statement write at least one sentence that supports or provides details for that statement.

1. Women were subordinate to men.
   Example: The son in a family had authority over all his sisters, and women were expected to walk ten steps behind their husbands in public.

2. Marriages were arranged for practical reasons.
   Example: Marriages were arranged to benefit the social position or wealth of the families involved, not for romance.

3. Among the upper classes, a woman's beauty was considered more important than her health.
   Example: Young girls underwent foot-binding, which crippled them, in order to be considered "beautiful."

4. The Chinese family had an authoritarian structure.
   Example: In a Chinese family, the oldest male had the final word in all family matters; the grandmother had authority over all the women.

5. Families assumed some duties that the police or judicial systems take care of in many countries.
   Example: When conflicts arose between members of different families, the families involved settled them.

6. Wang Anshi tried to improve the management of Chinese government.
   Example: He improved the university system to produce better officials, made civil service examinations more practical, and reformed the merit system to reduce corruption.

7. Advances in farming technologies meant that Song China could support a larger population.
   Example: The moldboard and new strains of rice led to increased productivity which allowed the population almost to double during the Song dynasty.

© Scott, Foresman and Company

WORKSHEET
Chapter 16, Section 3
The Mongols

Part A

For each set of statements below, write **F** for fact and **O** for opinion.

1. a. __F__ Kublai Khan moved his capital city to Beijing and adopted Chinese ways.

   b. __O__ If Mongols had kept to their own traditions, the Chinese would have hated them less.

2. a. __O__ Kublai Khan's naval expeditions against Japan were doomed to failure.

   b. __F__ Kublai Khan's ships were destroyed off Japan's coast by typhoons.

3. a. __F__ People in Italy did not believe Marco Polo's accounts of the wealth and size of China.

   b. __O__ Europeans probably would not have visited China for many centuries without Marco Polo's trip to arouse their interest.

4. a. __F__ Europeans learned about printing and the use of gunpowder from the Chinese.

   b. __O__ Eventually, Europeans themselves would have invented gunpowder and printing.

5. a. __F__ The Mongols ruled an empire that spanned most of Eurasia.

   b. __O__ The Mongols were the most despicable barbarians who ever lived.

6. a. __F__ During the Mongol period, Chinese inventions were transmitted across Eurasia to other civilizations.

   b. __O__ During the Mongol period, the Chinese progressed as a result of contact with the rest of Eurasia.

Part B

What do you see as the effects of Mongolian rule on China? Support your answer.

As Mongolian rule increased the safety of travel and trade across Eurasia, inventions and ideas were more easily spread from one end of the continent to the other. During the rule of Kublai Khan, roads were built, provisions were made for times of famine and for the sick and orphaned, and palaces were built. However, the rule of the Mongols intensified the Chinese's dislike of foreigners and probably increased their isolationist tendencies.

_____

_____

_____

WORKSHEET
Chapter 16, Section 4

In this worksheet you
will review important
events in Vietnamese and
Korean history.

Korean and Vietnamese Milestones

Using the numbers **1** through **8**, arrange the events in chronological order. On the
lines after each event, tell why it was an important happening.

a. __2__ The Chinese seized control of Vietnam.
**Possible answer: The Vietnamese imitated Chinese art and literature
and adopted Confucian social and religious ideas.**

b. __7__ Vietnam was wracked by civil war.
**Possible answer: The strife weakened the country, making it an easy
target for European colonial powers a century later.**

c. __1__ Many Chinese moved into northern Korea.
**Possible answer: The Koreans adopted and modified Chinese
agricultural techniques and the Chinese writing system.**

d. __5__ The Vietnamese defeated Kublai Khan.
**Possible answer: The defeat prevented the Mongols from
overrunning Southeast Asia.**

e. __3__ The Kingdom of Silla unified Korea.
**Possible answer: The Silla period, Korea's Golden Age, saw Koreans
absorb Chinese art and literature, as well as Buddhism.**

f. __4__ The Koryo took over from the Silla.
**Possible answer: The Koryo undertook many reforms, including
revival of a civil service system, redistribution of land, and increased
availability of education.**

g. __6__ King Sejong reigned in Korea.
**Possible answer: He instituted many social reforms and oversaw a
second Golden Age during which the Korean alphabet was
developed.**

Name _____   Date _____

Chapter 17, Section 1

In this worksheet you will review the ways in which Japan's geography influenced its history.

Geographic Features of Japan

Part A
Write the letter of the word or words from the box that best complete each sentence.

1. Japan's four largest islands are Honshu, Kyushu, Hokkaido, and __e__.

2. About 100 miles of sea separate Japan from __f__.

3. About 500 miles of sea separate Japan from __g__.

4. The __d__ has served as both a barrier to invaders and as a lane for travel.

5. Its distance from __h__ has allowed Japan to isolate itself but also to borrow from other civilizations.

6. Japan lies within a region of intense volcanic activity called __b__.

7. Japan's location has made it subject to the seasonal arrival of __c__.

8. One of the most impressive sights in Japan is __a__.

9. About 70 percent of Japan is covered by __i__.

10. Japan's native religion of __j__ holds nature to be sacred.

a. Mt. Fuji	**f.** Korea
b. the Pacific Ring of Fire	**g.** mainland China
c. typhoons	**h.** the Asian mainland
d. Sea of Japan	**i.** mountains
e. Shikoku	**j.** Shintoism

Part B
Write only the numbers of true statements on the blanks and add up the numbers.
The total should be 17.

1. __1__ Japan has been greatly affected by its climate and terrain.

2. _____ Japan never borrowed from its Asian neighbors.

3. __3__ Japan sometimes chose to shut out the outside world.

4. _____ Typhoons are a rare form of volcanic explosion.

5. __5__ Japan's location on the Pacific Ring of Fire is responsible for its typhoons, earthquakes, and volcanic eruptions.

6. _____ Japan is made up of 11 islands.

7. _____ The Sea of Japan separates Japan from Korea.

8. __8__ Mt. Fuji is an inactive volcano.

WORKSHEET

Chapter 17, Section 2

In this worksheet you will review facts about early Japanese civilization.

Early Japanese Civilization

Part A
Use information from the text to complete each of the following sentences.

1. The Japanese had great reverence for the emperor **because**
   Possible answer: they believed that he was of divine origin, descended from the Sun Goddess.

2. Shinto shrines honor important features of nature **because**
   Possible answer: the Shinto faith holds that nature has to be understood and reverenced.

3. The Japanese did not adopt the Chinese examination system for selecting civil servants **because**
   Possible answer: they believed that government officials should be chosen on the basis of birth and social rank.

4. Almost all prose writers of the Heian period were women **because**
   Possible answer: Japanese women were not taught to write by using the Chinese characters; instead, they wrote in their native language using kana.

5. By the 12th century, the emperor had lost much of his authority **because**
   Possible answer: creation of tax-free estates reduced the central government's tax support, which in turn weakened the emperor's power.

Part B
Imagine that you are Prince Shotoku and that your official delegation to China has just returned to Japan. Write a formal speech welcoming the delegation home.
Student speeches should reflect enthusiasm for all things Chinese and express the desire to see Japan adopt Chinese institutions and ways.

WORKSHEET

Chapter 17, Section 3

Feudalism in Japan

In this worksheet you
will review important
terms and main ideas
about Japan's feudal
period.

Part A

Write the letter of the correct description or definition of each name or term from
the box.

1. __b__ Kamakura

2. __g__ samurai

3. __e__ Kamikaze

4. __f__ Ashikaga Shogunate

5. __h__ Minamoto Yoritomo

6. __d__ daimyo

7. __c__ Sesshu

8. __a__ shogun

| a. hereditary feudal ruler of Japan |
| b. Yorimoto's seat of government |
| c. Buddhist monk who gained fame as an artist |
| d. local nobles during Ashikaga period |
| e. typhoon that destroyed the supply ships of Mongol invaders |
| f. period in Japanese history when the shogun did not control his vassals |
| g. Japanese warriors |
| h. first shogun |

Part B

Write **C** next to each phrase that correctly completes the unfinished sentence. (Each
incomplete sentence may have more than one correct ending.)

1. Samurai

   a. __C__ had a moral tie to the shogun.

   b. _____ were not known for their skill in battle.

   c. __C__ followed a strict code of conduct.

   d. _____ preferred the lance as a weapon.

2. The office of shogun

   a. __C__ began in 1192 with the rule of Yoritomo.

   b. __C__ became hereditary.

   c. _____ eliminated the role of emperor.

   d. __C__ resembled the role of lord in the European feudal system.

3. An important element of Japanese culture is

   a. __C__ a special interest in poetry.

   b. __C__ the art of flower arrangement.

   c. _____ elaborate architecture.

   d. __C__ the performance of No dramas.

4. During the Kamakura Shogunate,

   a. _____ all daimyo had to live in Edo every other year.

   b. __C__ the Mongols attempted to invade Japan.

   c. _____ Portugese ships brought missionaries and European products to Japan.

   d. __C__ Yoritomo became the shogun of all Japan.

WORKSHEET
Chapter 17, Section 4

Japanese Family Life

In this worksheet you
will consider the ways
that Japanese family life
differs from your own.

Part A
Imagine that you are the teenage daughter of a typical Japanese family in the 10th century. Write **Y** next to each phrase that describes an activity you might perform.

1. _____ come downstairs in the morning
2. __Y__ heat charcoal in the hibachi
3. __Y__ fold and put away mattresses and blankets
4. _____ discuss politics with your father
5. _____ prepare a roast for dinner
6. _____ rearrange the furniture
7. __Y__ arrange flowers in their alcoves
8. __Y__ write poetry

Part B
Make a list of usual activities that members of your family perform in your kitchen and a list of activities that members of a Japanese family living before the Tokugawa period probably would have performed. Tell how these differ from each other.

Students' lists may include many tasks related to cooking and to eating.

Differences may refer to methods of food preparation, food products,

and mealtimes.

_____

_____

_____

_____

_____

_____

_____

_____

_____

_____

_____

_____

WORKSHEET
Chapter 18, Section 1

In this worksheet you will
review the kingdoms of
Ghana, Mali, and Songhai.

Three West African Empires

Part A
Identify each of the following and briefly explain its significance in the history of
the West African empires.

1. Sudan
   **Possible answer: The Sudan was the home of the three powerful
   West African empires of Ghana, Mali, and Songhai.**

2. salt deposit at Taghaza
   **Possible answer: West Africans' need for salt determined that
   Taghaza became a major stop on the trade routes.**

3. the "ship of the desert"
   **Possible answer: By means of the camel, the "ship of the desert,"
   merchants crossed the Sahara to trade.**

4. the gold mines of Wangara
   **Possible answer: The gold mines in the forests of Wangara were the
   source of wealth for the West African kingdoms.**

5. Timbuktu
   **Possible answer: Timbuktu, a city of the Mali Empire, became a
   center of scholarship in the 14th and 15th centuries.**

Part B
In the blank before each item below, write the letter from the time line that matches
the date of the item.

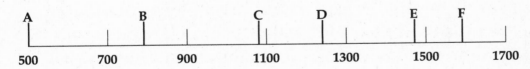

A		B		C	D		E	F	
500	700	900	1100	1300	1500	1700

1. __C__ The Almoravids attacked Kumbi-Saleh.
2. __E__ Sonni Ali captured Timbuktu.
3. __D__ Sundiata conquered the last king of Ghana.
4. __A__ The kingdom of Ghana began to develop.
5. __F__ The Moroccans defeated the Songhai.
6. __B__ Islam spread to West Africa.

WORKSHEET
Chapter 18, Section 2

Zimbabwe and the Port Cities

Part A
Write **T** if the statement is true and **F** if it is false. On the lines below, rewrite each false statement to make it true.

1. __F__ People from India and the Arabian peninsula first sailed westward as missionaries.

2. __T__ The trade winds created predictable shipping routes.

3. __T__ Asian porcelain was demanded by East Africans, who displayed it in their homes.

4. __T__ Port cities developed on the East African coast as African and Middle Eastern traders settled there.

5. __T__ Kilwa merchants grew rich by trading gold.

6. __T__ Swahili culture resulted from interchange among African, Indian, and Arab traders.

7. __F__ The predominant religion of the Swahili people was Islam.

8. __T__ The Swahili sought good trade relations with distant lands.

1. Possible answer: People from India and the Arabian peninsula first sailed westward looking for new sources of trade.

7. Possible answer: Although some converted to Islam, most Swahili people continued to practice native African religions.

Part B
Write a significant effect of each development below.

1. Islam and Islamic trade spread in the 7th century.
   Possible answer: East African and Indian Ocean trade flourished, stimulating the growth of East African ports into city-states and the rise of kingdoms such as Zimbabwe in the interior of East Africa.

2. The East African city-states had few defenses and no guns.
   Possible answer: The Portuguese were able to subdue the city-states fairly easily.

3. The Portuguese destroyed the governments and trade networks of East Africa.
   Possible answer: The destruction led to a decline in trade, although Swahili culture survived.

WORKSHEET
Chapter 18, Section 3

Forest States

Part A

Write **C** next to each phrase that correctly completes the unfinished sentence.
(Each incomplete sentence may have more than one correct ending.)

1. Both corn and cassava

   _____ were taken from Africa to the Americas by the Portuguese.

   __C__ grew easily in the African forest.

   __C__ became a staple food of the forest peoples.

   __C__ were responsible for increasing the forest peoples' population.

2. Slavery in the African states

   __C__ had always been permitted.

   _____ was based on race and skin color.

   _____ was always a lifelong status.

   __C__ was a penalty for prisoners of war, debtors, and convicts.

3. The forest states of Benin, Dahomey, Kongo, and Asante

   __C__ had flourishing agriculture and trade.

   __C__ survived until the late 1800s.

   __C__ aquired wealth from their trade in human beings.

   _____ were located along the eastern coast of Africa.

4. The Middle Passage

   __C__ was the sea voyage of slaves bound for America.

   __C__ lasted for ten weeks or more.

   __C__ resulted in the death of many slaves.

   _____ was a march across the interior of Africa.

5. The Obas of Benin

   __C__ were religious rulers.

   __C__ were sometimes women.

   __C__ allowed no Europeans to live in Benin.

   __C__ ruled a materially advanced African culture.

6. After the development of a plantation economy in the West Indies, African slaves

   __C__ were taken in village raids.

   _____ sometimes became advisers to kings.

   __C__ were sold to Europeans by African merchants.

   __C__ were used as the main labor force.

Part B

Write the letter of the name from the box next to its identifying phrase.

1. __c__ had one of the largest buildings in Benin for a palace

2. __d__ described the city of Benin

3. __a__ built a new capital and named it Benin

4. __e__ paid taxes and import dues to Benin

5. __b__ expanded the state and made Benin a fortified city

a. Oba Ewedo
b. Eware the Great
c. queen mother of Benin
d. Dutch geographer
e. European traders

Name _____ Date _____

WORKSHEET

Chapter 18, Section 4

In this worksheet you will review the development of the Aztec and the Inca civilizations.

Early American Cultures

Part A
Identify the Indian civilization described by each phrase. Write **I** for Inca and **A** for Aztec. Write **IA** if the phrase applies to both.

1. __IA__ were polytheistic

2. __IA__ practiced human sacrifice

3. __A__ built a magnificent city at Tenochtitlán

4. __I__ had no written language

5. __I__ settled in the valley of the Andes

6. __I__ named their capital Cuzco

7. __IA__ conquered distant regions

8. __I__ absorbed conquered peoples into their own culture

9. __I__ used quipus to keep records

10. __A__ wrote history in a kind of book called a codex

Part B
Select one of the two statements below as a topic sentence for a paragraph.
Complete your paragraph by writing supporting or detail sentences.

Topic sentences: 1) Tenochtitlán had many striking features.
                     2) The Aztecs were a religious people.

Examples: 1) The city sat on islands in a shallow lake. Temples and pyramids adorned the city square. Most people lived in adobe houses that were painted white and trimmed with bright colors. In lively marketplaces, merchants sold fruits and vegetables, cloth and clothing, and jewelry. 2) The Aztecs had many gods, including the god of the sun and war, the rain god, and Quetzalcoatl, represented in the form of a feathered snake. They believed they needed to make continual human sacrifice in order to keep the universe alive and went to war to take prisoners for that purpose. They also trained sons of nobles and rich merchants—and even some women—to become priests.

© Scott, Foresman and Company

WORKSHEET
Chapter 18, Section 5

North American Indians

Part A
Each of the following phrases refers to one North American Indian culture. Identify the culture by writing **NP** for North Pacific Coast, **W** for Woodland (Iroquois), or **P** for Pueblo.

1. __P__ made excellent pottery and finely woven cloth
2. __P__ built adobe homes
3. __W__ lived in wigwams
4. __P__ include the Hopi and Zuñi
5. __NP__ were hunters, gatherers, and fishermen
6. __P__ lived in what is now the southwestern United States
7. __NP__ constructed wooden houses
8. __W__ had a confederation called the Five Nations

Part B
Write a cause for each effect.

1. The North Pacific Coast Indians built wooden houses.
   Possible answer: This group utilized a plentiful natural resource—trees—to construct their homes.

2. In the 1600s some Indians, such as the Sioux and Cheyenne, became buffalo hunters.
   Possible answer: The introdution of the horse by the Spanish made it possible for Indians to hunt buffalo.

3. The Pueblo stored reserves of food and developed irrigation.
   Possible answer: Their natural environment, a dry land constantly menaced by drought, led the Pueblo to take steps to alleviate the problems caused by lack of water.

WORKSHEET

Chapter 19, Section 1

The Italian Renaissance

Part A

Write the letter of the name or phrase from the box next to its definition or identifying phrase.

1. __d__ the "Queen of the Adriatic," a powerful city-state with a large fleet of ships

2. __a__ a city famous for its art, whose wealth came from industry and banking

3. __f__ an economic system in which businesses are owned by private individuals or companies

4. __c__ receipts for payment of goods in one city that were exchanged for similar goods in another city

5. __g__ a wealthy banking family in Florence

6. __b__ the form of government in the Italian city-states

7. __h__ leaders of private bands of soldiers, many of whom became leaders in the city-states

8. __e__ leaders of cities who usually provided well-run governments but who often used force or trickery to seize or maintain power

a.	Florence
b.	republic
c.	bills of exchange
d.	Venice
e.	despots
f.	capitalism
g.	Medici
h.	condottieri

Part B

Use information from the text to complete each of the following sentences.

1. The Renaissance was mostly a secular movement **because**
   Possible answer: people came to believe that they perfect themselves and their societies through study of nonreligious ideas.

2. The Renaissance style emerged in Italy during the 14th century in part **because**
   Possible answer: trade brought wealth, with which people supported art and learning, to the Italian cities.

3. Italy could profit from the growing trade with the East **because**
   Possible answer: it was situated where most trade routes from the East converged.

4. Machiavelli stated that a ruler had to use every possible means to acquire and keep power **because**
   Possible answer: he realized that to be strong, a ruler had to keep the state stable and safe from its enemies at all costs.

WORKSHEET
Chapter 19, Section 2

Humanism in Italy

In this worksheet you will review information about Italian humanism.

Part A
Write the letter of the name from the box that best completes each sentence.

a.	Baldassare Castiglione
b.	Benvenuto Cellini
c.	Petrarch
d.	Giovanni Boccaccio
e.	Leonardo da Vinci

1. __c__ The Florentine writer regarded as the founder of Renaissance thought and literature is _____.

2. __d__ A famous humanist, _____, wrote the *Decameron*, a collection of stories that made fun of feudal customs and the Church.

3. __a__ The author of *The Courtier*, _____, outlined the characteristics of Renaissance men and women.

4. __e__ The painter of the *Mona Lisa*, _____, was also an engineer who designed buildings, canals, and weapons.

5. __b__ A brilliant sculptor and goldsmith, _____, cared little for laws or morals.

Part B
For each statement below, write two or three sentences that support or provide details for that statement.

1. Humanism had several meanings during the Renaissance.
Possible answer: Humanism encouraged the study of classical literature and languages as models for many aspects of life. Humanism reflected the optimistic view that men and women could change the world to make it a better place.

2. Petrarch was the founder of Renaissance thought and literature.
Possible answer: Petrarch's ideas about classical works influenced scholars and princes to collect and study ancient manuscripts. His belief that educated people should study history, languages, literature, and ethics gave birth to the view that education should expose people to all aspects of learning and experience.

3. Renaissance attitudes about the abilities of the individual gave people faith in their own powers.
Possible answer: People became inspired to search for knowledge in diverse fields and began to question Church authority. Some Renaissance people, such as Benvenuto Cellini, took the extreme view that the individual was the center of the world, thereby disregarding the laws and morals that regulate social activity.

WORKSHEET

Chapter 19, Section 3

Italian Renaissance Art

In this worksheet you
will review information
about the art of the Italian
Renaissance.

Part A
Identify the person described in each riddle by choosing the letter of the correct
name from the box.

a.	Titian
b.	Giovanni Bellini
c.	Michelangelo
d.	Donatello
e.	Raphael

1. __c__ Born near Florence, I was a painter, sculptor, architect, and a poet.
One of my toughest jobs but greatest achievements was painting
the Sistine Chapel ceiling while lying on my back. Who am I?

2. __b__ A native of Venice, I preferred to paint in a style that was soft and
gentle, although I liked vibrant colors. Who am I?

3. __e__ I was famous for painting religious subjects, especially Madonnas.
Popes Julius II and Leo X gave me work in the Vatican and
St. Peter's Church. Who am I?

4. __a__ My portraits have brought me fame, although my landscapes are
quality works of art. I was a student of Bellini's and learned to
capture the spirit of my subjects. Who am I?

5. __d__ As a sculptor in Florence, I carefully studied human anatomy to
sculpt human movement in a realistic manner. Who am I?

Part B
For each statement below, write two or three sentences that support or provide
details for that statement.

1. Renaissance painters broke from medieval artistic styles by creating realistic
human figures.
   **Possible answer: Giotto paved the way for change in the 1300s by
   making figures appear to move. Later Florentine artists drew human
   figures more accurately and used light and shadow to depict feelings
   and ideas in the face and body. They also developed perspective.**

2. By the early 1500s, Venetian painters had begun their own traditions.
   **Possible answer: Venetian painters became famous for their use of
   rich, glowing colors. Because of the dampness in Venice, they also
   began painting in oils on canvas rather than on walls.**

3. Renaissance sculpture followed much the same pattern as painting.
   **Possible answer: Like painters, sculptors began to create works of art
   that were naturalistic portraits of human beings. Donatello became the
   first sculptor of his time carefully to study human anatomy to perfect
   his art.**

WORKSHEET
Chapter 19, Section 4

The Northern European Renaissance

Write **T** if the statement is true and **F** if it is false. On the lines below, rewrite each false statement to make it true.

1. __T__ Before printing was invented, books were written by hand.

2. __F__ Johann Gutenberg invented the printing press independent of ideas from Europe or other parts of the world.

3. __T__ With the invention of the printing press, books became cheaper and literacy spread throughout Europe.

4. __F__ Northern humanists were most concerned with medical reforms.

5. __F__ Sir Thomas More was a priest who studied Greek and Latin writings and wrote *Praise of Folly*.

6. __F__ Desiderius Erasmus wanted to reform society and wrote *Utopia*.

7. __T__ Flemish painters used oil paints before the Italian Renaissance reached northern Europe.

8. __T__ Jan van Eyck is known for his realistic landscapes and paintings that incorporate religious symbols.

9. __F__ Shakespeare had a great command of the English language but lacked a feeling for the whole range of human emotions.

10. __T__ Both Shakespeare and Cervantes incorporated humanist ideas into their writings.

2. Possible answer: Johann Gutenberg developed a printing press that was based on the European wine press after the Chinese already had invented movable type.

4. Possible answer: Northern humanists were most concerned with social and religious problems.

5. Possible answer: Desiderius Erasmus was a priest who studied Greek and Latin writings and wrote *Praise of Folly*.

6. Possible answer: Sir Thomas More wanted to reform society and wrote *Utopia*.

9. Possible answer: Shakespeare had a deep understanding of human beings and expressed the whole range of human emotions in his plays.

WORKSHEET

Chapter 20, Section 1

In this worksheet you will review the explorations of Columbus and da Gama.

The Voyages of Columbus and da Gama

Under each headline write a short news article based on the information in your textbook.

Vol. I, No. 1	**History and Life Chronicle** Palos, Spain June, 1493	★ ★ ★ LATE EDITION

Columbus Will Make Second Voyage

Students' answers could mention Spanish monarchs' decision to fund a second voyage, their reaction to Columbus' previous success, and preparations and approximate dates for new sailing.

Last Year's Voyage Described

Students' answers could include questions that probe Columbus' difficulties on his first voyage or his observations about the significance of his journey.

Spain Hopes to Gain from Second Trip

Students' answers could include the following possible motives: desire for riches and new products, territorial gains, navigational and geographical knowledge, and glory for Spain.

Spain Challenges Portugal's Lead

Students' answers could be in the form of an editorial that points out the fierce rivalry between Spain and Portugal for reaching the East and argues that Spain recently has surpassed Portugal as the world leader in exploration.

Pope Will Mediate Between Spain and Portugal

Students' answers could describe the conflict between Spain and Portugal and relate the Spanish decision to ask the pope for rights to all newly discovered lands across the Atlantic.

BULLETIN: Da Gama Prepares to Sail East

Students' answers could mention Portuguese persistence in sailing eastward and da Gama's initial plans to follow the route of Bartolomeu Dias, then set his own course to reach India.

WORKSHEET

Chapter 20, Section 2

Explorers and Their Discoveries

In this worksheet you will review the major explorers of the early 16th century and the results of their discoveries.

Part A
Write the letter of the result from the box next to each expedition.

1. __b__ Balboa's expedition
2. __c__ Pizarro's conquest
3. __d__ Drake's attacks on Spanish ships
4. __e__ Cabot and Cartier's expeditions
5. __a__ Magellan's trip

> a. confirmation that one could reach the East Indies by sailing west
> b. the first permanent Spanish settlement on American mainland
> c. Spain's claim of Central America and most of South America
> d. the beginning of Spain's decline and England's dominance of the seas in the 17th century
> e. years of conflict between France and England over North American territory

Part B
Use information from the text to complete each of the following sentences.

1. _____ was the first European to view what is now called the Pacific Ocean.

2. _____ made expeditions that served as the basis of Spain's claim to southeastern North America.

3. The explorer who discovered the Grand Canyon was _____.

4. _____ died before finishing a grueling, three-year voyage around the world.

5. _____ claimed present-day Newfoundland for the king of England.

6. _____ combined exploration with piracy by preying on Spanish treasure ships.

Vasco de Balboa _____

Juan Ponce de León _____

Francisco de Coronado _____

Ferdinand Magellan _____

John Cabot _____

Sir Francis Drake _____

Part C
Explorers and their crews faced many hardships. For example, during Magellan's trip, food supplies were so low that the men ate leather and rats. Why do you think so many Europeans chose to accompany the explorers in the face of such hardship? Write an advertisement that might have appeared in a Spanish newspaper to entice sailors to join a new expedition.

Possible answer: Motives for explorers may include adventure, money, or escape from debts or other adverse conditions in Spain. The advertisement should stress the sense of adventure and material gain for new crew members.

WORKSHEET

Chapter 20, Section 3

Five Colonial Empires

In this worksheet you will review the colonizing patterns of England, France, Spain, Portugal, and the Netherlands.

Part A

Identify the country or countries to which each statement applies. Write **N** for the Netherlands, **P** for Portugal, **S** for Spain, **E** for England, and **F** for France.

1. **P, N** Its small population kept it from establishing many colonies.

2. **S, E** Its large population allowed it to establish secure colonies with settlers from the homeland.

3. **F** It established a profitable fur-trading empire in North America.

4. **F** Its religious minorities were not allowed to settle in its colonies, thus hindering it from developing a lasting empire in the Americas.

5. **P** It gained the Indian Ocean spice trade in the early 1500s.

6. **N** It took over much of the Indian Ocean spice trade in the late 1500s.

7. **P** Even after it lost the profitable spice trade, it held on to colonies in China, India, Africa, and Brazil.

8. **S** Its explorers conquered the Aztecs and the Incas.

9. **P, N** Its empire was based on establishing and maintaining trading posts around the world.

10. **E** Its religious minorities, who were seeking a life free of persecution, proved ideal colonists.

11. **N, E** Its government granted a private company a charter and special trading rights.

12. **E** In time, it took over the whole Indian subcontinent.

Part B

Number the events in the order in which they happened.

6 Robert de la Salle claimed Louisiana for France.

1 The Dutch founded the Dutch East Indies Company.

5 Louis Joliet and Jacques Marquette explored the Great Lakes region for France.

2 The English built their first successful settlement at Jamestown.

3 Samuel de Champlain established the first permanent French settlement in North America at Quebec.

4 The Dutch set up a trading colony along the Hudson River.

WORKSHEET
Chapter 20, Section 4

In this worksheet you will review some key economic issues of the Age of Exploration.

The Economy of the Age of Exploration

Part A
Present at least two specific facts from your text to support each statement.

1. Spain exploited the wealth of the Americas and then choked on it.
   Example: Spain imported so much gold and silver that demand for goods increased rapidly, causing inflation. As the amount of precious metals declined in the 1600s, Spanish power fell dramatically.

2. Although slavery had existed during other historical periods, the nature of slavery gradually changed in North America.
   Example: Previously, slavery had been regarded as a temporary legal condition. In North America, the belief evolved that slavery was a permanent status based on African birth or heritage.

3. During the Age of Exploration, diets changed in many parts of the world.
   Example: Ships transported crops that became staples in other than their areas of origin. Potatoes, corn, sweet potatoes, and manioc from the New World became staples in Europe, Africa, and Asia.

Part B
Use the diagram and your text to answer the questions.

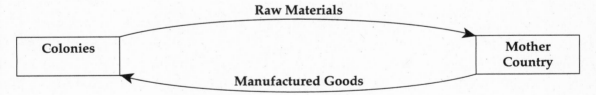

Raw Materials

Colonies   Mother Country

Manufactured Goods

1. The diagram shows how the existence of colonies might further a country's mercantilist goals. What idea underlies mercantilism?
   Mercantilism is based on the idea that for a country to be strong, it must export more than it imports.

2. How might colonies be important for a mercantilist nation?
   Possible answer: They provide raw materials and serve as closed markets for manufactured goods.

3. Why might colonies feel that the rules enforcing closed markets worked to their own economic disadvantage?
   Possible answer: These rules limited what colonists could purchase and what industries they could develop.

WORKSHEET
Chapter 21, Section 1
The Church Loses Power

In this worksheet you will review terms dealing with what you have learned about the Catholic Church.

Read the clues below and complete the crossword puzzle.

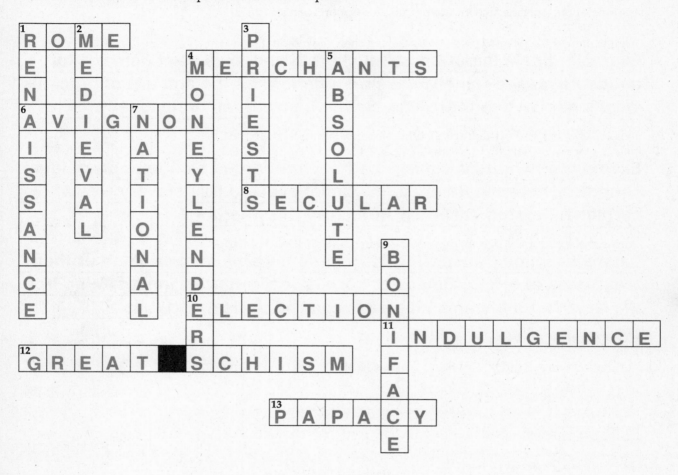

Across
1. the traditional home of the papacy
4. businessmen; a class that challenged Church power
6. papal city in 1309
8. the kind of ideas fostered by the rise of cities
10. the method of choosing one pope that was demanded by the Holy Roman Emperor
11. church document said to free sinners from punishment after death
12. name given to the 1378 division in the Church (two words)
13. supreme Church authority whose status had fallen by 1417

Down
1. a period of cultural rebirth in the Italian cities
2. age when the Church reached the height of its power
3. churchmen claimed by Boniface to be above royal law
4. an urban business group whose activities were forbidden by the medieval Church
5. the kind of power Boniface claimed for the pope
7. the kind of church that people in England and Germany began to want
9. the arrogant pope who declared the pope's absolute power; _____ VIII

WORKSHEET
Chapter 21, Section 2

In this worksheet you
will review important
Reformation leaders and
their beliefs.

Reformation Leaders

Part A
Identify the Protestant religious leader most likely to make each statement by
writing **L** for Luther or **C** for Calvin.

1. __C__ Those who would be saved were "elected" or "predestined" by God.
2. __L__ Salvation is based on faith alone, and faith comes through God's grace.
3. __L__ All believers are priests in their own right.
4. __C__ Correct behavior might produce clues as to who is among the elect.
5. __L__ Indulgences have no value since sins can be forgiven only by faith.
6. __L__ The Bible is the ultimate religious authority, and people can interpret
   it themselves.
7. __C__ All people deserve punishment in hell.

Part B
Only three of the four items in each group are related in some way. Circle the item
that does not belong and explain how the remaining three items are related.

1. Luther   Calvin   King Henry VIII   (Pope Leo X)

   **Possible answer: Luther, Calvin, and King Henry VIII all founded
   Protestant churches.**

2. church services   pilgrimages   (epistles)   indulgences

   **Possible answer: Luther believed that church services, pilgrimages,
   and indulgences could not bring salvation.**

3. Bible   (simony)   printing press   Ninety-five Theses

   **Possible answer: The printing press enabled lay people to read
   Luther's Ninety-five Theses and the Bible in translation.**

4. Counter Reformation   Council of Trent   Ignatius Loyola   (Anglican Church)

   **Possible answer: During the Counter Reformation, Ignatius Loyola's
   Jesuits and the reforms of the Council of Trent helped the Catholic
   Church to regain some of its lost prestige.**

WORKSHEET
Chapter 21, Section 3
Religious and Political Conflict

Part A

Read the statements below. Write **T** if the statement is true and **F** if it is false. On the lines below, rewrite each false statement to make it true.

1. **T** Philip II used the Inquisition to destroy Protestantism.

2. **T** The Hapsburg family was the strongest power in Europe during the 16th century.

3. **F** The Holy Roman Emperor Charles V had absolute control of the rulers of Germany during the Reformation period.

4. **F** Queen Mary advanced Protestantism, and Elizabeth I promoted Catholicism in England.

3. Possible answer: Charles V had power only in name over the rulers of Germany during the Reformation period.

4. Possible answer: England was Catholic under Queen Mary's rule and Protestant under Elizabeth I's reign.

Part B

Read the following excerpts from the Edict of Nantes and complete the exercises.

VI. We permit those of the so-called Reformed Religion to live and abide in all the towns and districts of this our Realm . . . free from inquisition, molestation or compulsion to do anything in the way of religion, against their conscience . . . .

XVIII. We forbid all our subjects . . . to take children of this religion, by force or persuasion to be baptized or confirmed in the Catholic Apostolic and Roman Church.

XXVII. Members of this religion are capable of holding any office or position in this Realm.

1. Identify the "Reformed Religion" mentioned in the Edict.
   Possible answers: Protestantism; the Huguenot faith

2. What is one action that the Edict specifically forbade?
   Possible answers: forced baptism or confirmation of Huguenot children; compulsion of Huguenots to act against conscience

3. What do you think the Edict means by the phrase "free from inquisition"?
   Possible answer: Protestants should not be questioned, terrorized, or harassed because of their beliefs.

5. Henry IV of France reportedly remarked after converting to Catholicism that "Paris is worth a Mass." What do you think he meant?
   Possible answer: He meant that his conversion to Catholicism was motivated by a desire to promote national unity.

WORKSHEET
Chapter 21, Section 4

Absolute Monarchy in France

Part A
Complete each statement with the explanations given in your text.

1. Absolutism appealed to Europeans in the 17th century **because**
   Possible answer: they wanted powerful governments that could keep the peace.

2. In *Leviathan*, Hobbes claimed that human beings needed absolutism **because**
   Possible answer: humans were basically selfish and greedy, and without strong controls, they would always be at war.

3. Louis XIII allowed Cardinal Richelieu to act with almost absolute power over France **because**
   Possible answer: the young Louis XIII found he could not manage the country without the already powerful Richelieu.

4. France fought the Thirty Years' War **because**
   Possible answer: Richelieu wanted to weaken the Hapsburgs in order to make the French king the most powerful ruler in Europe.

5. At the end of Louis XIV's reign, France was left with an empty treasury **because**
   Possible answer: Louis XIV spent great sums on luxury and unsuccessful wars during his reign.

6. Louis XIV took away freedom of worship from the Huguenots **because**
   Possible answer: he believed that non-Catholics would be disloyal to France and would weaken the country.

Part B
Number the events in the order in which they happened.

   2   Richelieu became chief minister of France.

   1   Henry IV died.

   5   Louis XIV cancelled Edict of Nantes.

   4   Cardinal Mazarin died.

   3   *Leviathan* was published.

WORKSHEET
Chapter 21, Section 5

Absolute Monarchs in Eastern Europe

Part A
Write the letter of the name from the box next to its identifying phrase.

1. __e__ conquered areas south of Russia

2. __b__ built an absolutist Hapsburg monarchy

3. __a__ waged war against the Swedes to obtain "windows on the West"

4. __c__ raised the status of Prussia to that of a major power

5. __d__ chosen by a popular assembly to be tsar, ending the Time
of Troubles

6. __f__ invaded Silesia and helped destroy Poland as an independent nation

> a. Peter the Great
> b. Leopold I
> c. Frederick William
> d. Mikhail Romanov
> e. Catherine the Great
> f. Frederick II

Part B
Read the following poem in praise of Peter I written by the Russian poet Mikhail Lomonosov sometime before 1747.

Inscription for a Statue of Peter the Great

Behold the sculpture here of him, who, most audacious,
Most wise, forewent his ease to serve, supremely gracious,
Toward his people: chose the rank of lowliest knave,
And reigned—exemplar, he upheld the laws he gave; . . .

He built a city; none bore battle's brunt as he;
He visited far lands, and journeyed oversea;
To gather artists, to train soldiers was his doing,
The enemies at home, as those abroad, subduing:
There's Peter, father of the fatherland, in brief;
An earthly deity our Russia is adoring;
Many the altar fires before this figure soaring,
The hearts beholden to him, many beyond belief.

Use your text to find examples of Peter's actions to which the poet alludes.

a. "chose the rank of lowliest knave"
   Peter worked as a carpenter in a Dutch shipyard.

b. "built a city"
   constructed a new capital at St. Petersburg

c. "visited far lands"
   visited Germany and Sweden

d. "bore battle's brunt"
   waged the Great Northern War against Sweden

WORKSHEET
Chapter 22, Section 1

Scientists and the Scientific Method

Part A
Read each description below. Underline any factual errors you find and correct them on the lines below.

1. Sir Francis Bacon supported the scientific method: experiment, observe carefully, and record the results. In his view, once an experiment was completed, the experiment did not have to be repeated.

2. Réne Descartes was a mathematician who believed in truth based on logical thinking and experimentation. His ideas had an enormous influence on European thinkers of his time and form the basis of modern science.

3. Copernicus believed that the earth circled the sun. This was in direct contradiction to Ptolemy's belief, which was supported by the churches. However, the Copernican theory gained quick acceptance, because it was based on common sense.

4. Galileo's discoveries formed the basis for modern geology. By experimentation, Galileo discovered that mathematics can be used to explain the movement of objects through space and time.

1. **Possible answer: Bacon believed that the information should be tested by repeating experiments or creating new experiments.**

3. **Possible answer: The Copernican theory, based on mathematical tables, not common sense, was not accepted at first.**

4. **Possible answer: Galileo's discoveries formed the basis for modern physics.**

Part B
Write the letter of the term from the box next to its identifying phrase.

1. __d__ Leonardo da Vinci's description of the experiment

2. __b__ Galileo's description of his own and Copernicus' theories

3. __c__ Copernicus' theory that the sun is the center of the solar system and the earth and planets move around it

4. __a__ the oval path followed by the planets

5. __e__ Ptolemy's belief that the earth was fixed and the heavenly bodies moved around it

6. __f__ Kepler's scheme of the solar system

> a. ellipse
> b. *Dialogue on the Two Great Systems of the World*
> c. heliocentric theory
> d. "the mother of certainty"
> e. geocentric theory
> f. three laws of planetary motion

WORSHEET

Chapter 22, Section 2

Scientists and Their Discoveries

Choose words from the box to complete the chart.

Scientist	Accomplishment	Importance of Accomplishment
John Napier	**invented logarithms**	allowed mathematicians to calculate large numbers quickly
Gabriel Fahrenheit	**invented the first modern mercury thermometer**	made accurate measurement of termperature possible
Otto von Guericke	**invented first air pump capable of creating a vacuum**	**led to development of the steam engine**
Christian Huygens	**invented pendulum clock**	**allowed scientists correctly to measure small units of time**
Sir Isaac Newton	**developed theory of gravity**	**explained why planets do not fly off into space**
Robert Boyle	**first used the scientific method in chemistry**	**transformed alchemy into the scientific study of chemistry**
William Gilbert	**used sulfur and glass to create static electricity**	contributed to the understanding of electricity
Benjamin Franklin	**invented first lightning rod**	contributed to the understanding of electricity

first used the scientific method in chemistry
invented first air pump capable of creating
  a vacuum
explained why planets do not fly off
  into space
led to development of the steam engine
invented pendulum clock
invented the first modern mercury thermometer

invented logarithms
allowed scientists correctly to measure small units
  of time
transformed alchemy into the scientific study
  of chemistry
invented first lightning rod
developed theory of gravity
used sulfur and glass to create static electricity

WORKSHEET
Chapter 22, Section 3

The New Medicine

In this worksheet you will review the impact of the Age of Reason on the study of medicine.

Part A

For each set of statements below, write **M** before the main idea and **S** before any statements that support or help to explain the main idea. One statement in each set is not related to the main idea; write **X** next to this statement.

Set 1

_S_ Paracelsus suggested treatment of diseases with medicines derived from minerals.

_S_ Paracelsus believed that poisons caused most diseases.

_M_ Paracelsus disagreed with the medical thought of his day.

_X_ Paracelsus was born in Switzerland in 1493.

_S_ Paracelsus stated that the causes of most diseases could be discovered by observation.

Set 2

_S_ Vesalius' methods of learning anatomy soon became the standard for modern medical studies.

_S_ Vesalius sometimes robbed the gallows for dead bodies.

_X_ Vesalius was able to describe the human body correctly.

_M_ Vesalius challenged Galen's theories about anatomy.

_S_ Vesalius became a pioneer in anatomy.

Set 3

_S_ By using the microscope, physicians learned about the body and the causes of disease.

_X_ Leeuwenhoek's descriptions led to the belief that germs cause disease.

_S_ The microscope might have been invented by an eyeglass maker.

_S_ The discovery of the microscope led to many discoveries in medicine.

_M_ The microscope allowed scientists to examine tiny organisms.

Set 4

_S_ The discoveries of the Age of Reason were based on the scientific and intellectual advances of the 17th century.

_M_ The natural sciences flourished during the Age of Reason.

_S_ The scientific method enabled people to make discoveries about the universe.

_X_ The ancient Greeks were the first to set forth scientific theories.

_S_ During the Age of Reason, scientists' discoveries showed that the universe was a well-ordered machine, working according to the laws of nature.

Part B

Number the events in the order in which they happened.

_3_ Vesalius published *On the Fabric of the Human Body*.

_4_ Harvey explained how the heart works.

_5_ Leeuwenhoek worked with microscopes.

_6_ The Age of Reason reached its height.

_2_ Paracelsus broke with the ideas of the Greeks.

_1_ Galen developed his theories about anatomy.

WORKSHEET
Chapter 23, Section 1

The Ottoman Turks

In this worksheet you
will review the culture
and history of the
Ottoman Turks.

Part A
Fill in the blanks, using information given in your text.

The culture of the Ottoman Turks included a distinctive style of architecture and

interior design. The Turks often turned churches into ____**mosques**____

and combined features of Islamic architecture with those of the peoples they

conquered. For example, the Ottomans preserved and modified the most famous

church in Constantinople, ____**Hagia Sophia**____. A pattern developed in

Ottoman architecture; a mosque or palace would have several small

____**domes**____ surrounding a central ____**dome**____, with four

to six ____**minarets**____, or towers, at the building's edges. Inside, the walls

and floors were covered with ____**mosaics**____. Ottoman homes were also

impressive, with costly carpets, intricately designed tables, and brass tea urns called

____**samovars**____. The style was simple, yet magnificent at the same time.

Part B
Write **T** if the statement is true and **F** if it is false. On the lines below, rewrite each
false statement to make it true.

1. ___**T**___ The defeat of Constantinople in 1453 by the Ottoman Turks marked the
fall of the Byzantine Empire.

2. ___**F**___ After the Turks conquered Constantinople, they renamed the city Byzantium.

3. ___**T**___ The Children's Levy gave the Ottoman Turks an efficient recruiting system
for their army and state bureaucracy.

4. ___**F**___ Suleiman I is considered a great ruler because he united the Persians
and Afghans.

5. ___**T**___ One of the strengths of the Ottoman Empire was the organization of
its government.

6. ___**T**___ At its height the Ottoman Empire included parts of southern and eastern Europe,
Asia Minor to the Caspian Sea, and much of the northern coast of Africa.

**2. Possible answer: After the Turks conquered Constantinople, they
named the city Istanbul.**

**4. Possible answer: Suleiman I is considered a great ruler because of
his legal reforms, wisdom in diplomacy, patronage of the arts, and
military conquests.**

WORKSHEET
Chapter 23, Section 2
The Safavids in Persia

Part A

The Safavid dynasty established a unified Persia. Indicate which of the following three Safavid rulers was responsible for each action or accomplishment listed below.

A. Sheikh Safi   **B.** Ismail   **C.** Shah Abbas

1. **B** set out to conquer the world as an orphaned 13-year-old
2. **C** built a capital city at Isfahan
3. **B** encouraged Shiites in Asia Minor to rebel against their Ottoman rulers
4. **A** founded a religious group in Persia and developed a militaristic following
5. **B** made Shiism the official religion of Persia
6. **C** created an efficient government that excluded the military
7. **C** encouraged free trade with the European powers and tolerated non-Muslim religions

Part B

Using the pair of words in each set, write a sentence describing Persia under the Safavids.

1. Sunni/Shiite

   Possible answer: Although most Persians were Sunni Muslims prior to Ismail's conquests, they became Shiite Muslims after Ismail forced them to convert.

2. 200 years/Ottoman-Safavid conflict

   Possible answer: The Ottoman-Safavid conflict over borders—a conflict in which neither side was completely successful—lasted for over 200 years.

3. military/shah

   Possible answer: The Persian military and the shah struggled for power at different times during the Safavid rule of Persia.

4. national unity/early Safavid rule

   Possible answer: The forging of a sense of national unity from the varied Persian peoples was the major result of early Safavid rule.

WORKSHEET

Chapter 23, Section 3

India Under Mughal Rule

In this worksheet you will review the Mughal rule of India.

Part A
Number the events in the order in which they happened.

__4__ Nur Jahan is exiled to Lahore.

__2__ Babur defeats the sultan at Delhi.

__6__ Aurangzeb claims authority over all of India.

__1__ Babur captures Kabul.

__3__ Akbar becomes ruler of all northern India.

__5__ Shah Jahan restores Islam as the state religion.

Part B
The following rulers were prominent in the rise and fall of the Mughal Empire.
Write **B** for Babur, **J** for Jahangir, **A** for Akbar, or **SJ** for Shah Jahan to identify the ruler described by each phrase.

1. __A__ tolerated the practice of religions other than Islam

2. __J__ allowed his wife to rule in his absence

3. __B__ was a descendant of Tamerlane and Genghis Khan

4. __SJ__ built a magnificent *taj* to the memory of his dead wife

5. __SJ__ built 52 palaces at Delhi

6. __SJ__ ended the religious freedom allowed by his grandfather

7. __B__ conquered Kabul and established Mughal rule in India

8. __SJ__ ruled during the high point of Mughal power in India

9. __A__ attempted to outlaw suttee

Part C
Write a paragraph contrasting the reigns of Akbar and Aurangzeb.

Possible answer: Akbar was a just ruler who tolerated different religions, supported free discussion, and united different peoples in a common loyalty to Mughal rule. Aurangzeb used force to acquire and maintain power. Rather than tolerating other religions, Aurangzeb sought to establish a Muslim state by suppressing other religions, especially Hinduism.

WORKSHEET

Chapter 23, Section 4

Islam in Africa

In this worksheet you will review the rise and fall of several Muslim states in West Africa.

Part A
Write the letter of the word or words from the box that best complete each sentence.

1. __h__ In the Sudan, the Fulani revolution was the largest and most famous _____.

2. __e__ Uthman dan Fodio was a leader of the _____.

3. __f__ The Hausa lived in independent _____.

4. __c__ In addition to trading forest products, the Hausa developed _____.

5. __b__ A jihad is best defined as a _____.

6. __g__ The state of Kanem developed east of _____.

7. __a__ Idris Alooma, ruler of Kanem-Bornu, imposed _____ throughout his territories.

8. __d__ Until the late 1500s few of the common people of the Sudan were _____.

9. __i__ The _____ is a product that, when chewed, enables one to go for long periods of time without food or water.

a.	Islamic law
b.	holy war
c.	handicraft industries
d.	Muslims
e.	Fulani
f.	city-states
g.	Lake Chad
h.	jihad
i.	kola nut

Part B
Write a cause for each effect.

1. During the 1600s the balance of trade and political power shifted to the south and east in Africa.
   Possible answer: The Moroccan army invaded and destroyed the kingdom of Songhai in West Africa, which had been the largest and strongest state in the region.

2. Ambassadors from the Ottoman Empire traveled to Kanem-Bornu.
   Possible answer: Kanem-Bornu had become the strongest state in Central Sudan.

3. The Fulani people rose up against the Hausa leaders.
   Possible answer: The Hausa had become increasingly corrupt and religiously lax, and Uthman dan Fodio provided the leadership necessary for the Hausa to revolt.

WORKSHEET

Chapter 24, Section 1

Ming Rule

Part A
Write the letter of each effect from the box next to its cause.

1. __e__ Ming land-redistribution program
2. __f__ Portuguese violation of Ming trade rules
3. __d__ 15th-century Chinese naval expeditions
4. __a__ Mongol rule of China
5. __c__ Hong Wu's defeat of the Mongols
6. __g__ the invasion from the north in 1644
7. __b__ restoration of civil service examinations

---

a. resentment of the "intruders"
b. an orderly government administered by scholar-bureaucrats
c. beginning of the Ming dynasty
d. recognition for China's glory throughout the countries around the Indian Ocean
e. lessening of crowded conditions in southern China
f. Ming policy of isolationism
g. end of the Ming dynasty

Part B
Using the numbers **1** through **5**, arrange the events in chronological order. On the lines after each event, tell why it was an important happening.

__3__ Cheng Ho led naval expeditions.
Possible answer: On his voyages, Cheng Ho reached over 50 countries that he acquainted with the idea of Chinese power and with Chinese products.

__5__ The Manchus invaded China.
Possible answer: The Manchus conquered the Mings in 1644, ending the Ming dynasty.

__1__ Discontent with Mongol rule grew.
Possible answer: Rebellions broke out and Hong Wu drove out the Mongol rulers and established the Ming dynasty, returning China to Chinese rule.

__4__ Portuguese sailors reached China.
Possible answer: The Portuguese violated strict Chinese trade laws, which led to a Chinese policy of isolationism.

__2__ The Ming emperors came to power.
Possible answer: The Ming dynasty brought China almost 300 years of peaceful prosperity.

WORKSHEET
Chapter 24, Section 2

In this worksheet you
will review Ming and
Manchu China.

The Ming and Manchu Periods

Part A
For each statement below, write one or two sentences that support or provide
details for that statement.

1. The Manchu dynasty maintained Chinese culture.
   **Possible answer: The Manchus kept the existing Chinese system of
   government. They did not try to blend cultures but kept Manchus and
   Chinese separate by strict laws.**

2. China had effective central government under the Manchus.
   **Possible answer: The government provided law and order and built
   roads and canals. It stored grain against famine, helped farmers to
   clear land for cultivation, and helped to develop industry.**

3. Like his grandfather, Qian Long was a great Manchu emperor.
   **Possible answer: Both reigned for many years and pursued policies
   that led to China's growth.**

4. By 1800 numerous signs of decline had appeared in Manchu China.
   **Possible answer: Corruption in the military and in the government, as
   well as growing food shortages, were signs of decline.**

Part B
In the blank before each item below, write the letter from the time line that matches
the date of the item.

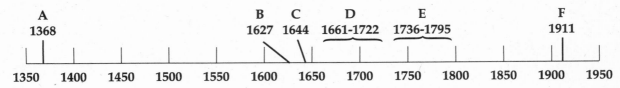

A	beginning of Ming dynasty
C	end of Ming dynasty; beginning of Manchu dynasty
F	end of Manchu dynasty
B	Manchu conquest of Korea
D	rule of Kangxi
E	rule of Qian Long; height of Manchu Empire

WORKSHEET
Chapter 24, Section 3

The Tokugawa Shogunate

Part A
Write the letter of the term from the box next to its definition or identifying phrase.

1. __c__ line of rulers who unified Japan in the 17th century
2. __f__ class of nobles
3. __d__ new headquarters of the Tokugawa shogun
4. __a__ a group that was expelled from Japan
5. __g__ old capital where emperors resided
6. __e__ first shogun of Tokugawa period
7. __h__ popular style of theater
8. __b__ world's first art for the masses

a. Christian missionaries
b. woodblock prints
c. Tokugawa Shogunate
d. Edo
e. Ieyasu
f. daimyo
g. Kyoto
h. Kabuki

Part B
Fill in the blanks with the terms or names from the box that best complete the sentences.

At the beginning of the Tokugawa Shogunate, Japan still had a _____feudal_____ way of life. Most of the population were _____serfs_____ who worked land held by their _____daimyo_____. When _____internal trade_____ increased, the population of _____cities_____ grew. In the cities the _____merchant_____ and _____business_____ classes became wealthy and influential. The _____Kabuki_____ style of theater was developed. By the end of the 1700s, Japan was evolving into a _____capitalistic_____ society and was ready for major changes. _____Samurai_____, whose power had been severely limited by the shoguns, were eager to see the Tokugawas removed from power.

cities	serfs	business
capitalistic	merchant	feudal
samurai	daimyo	internal trade
Kabuki		

     © Scott, Foresman and Company

WORKSHEET
Chapter 25, Section 1

In this worksheet you will review events of the Spanish and Portuguese conquests of the Americas.

The Conquest of the Americas

Part A
Use information from the text to complete each of the following sentences.

1. Along with his brothers, _____**Pizarro**_____ conquered and ruled the Inca Empire for 16 years.

2. Both Cortés and Pizarro sent out small groups of Spanish troops to widen their control, Cortés in _____**Central America**_____ and Pizarro in present-day _____**Ecuador**_____ and _____**Chile**_____.

3. _____**Cortés**_____ planned the seige of _____**Tenochtitlán**_____ that led to the conquest of the Aztec Empire.

4. The fight between Huascar and his brother _____**Atahualpa**_____ started a civil war and helped the Spanish to conquer the _____**Incas**_____.

5. The ruler _____**Montezuma**_____ made the mistake of believing the Spanish conquistador was an Aztec god.

6. After the Spaniards tricked _____**Atahualpa**_____ into paying a ransom in silver and gold, they killed him.

7. The _____**Portuguese**_____ settled Brazil and imported _____**black slaves**_____ to work on sugar plantations there.

Part B
Review the quotation from the letter by Huaman Poma in your text. Answer the questions below.

1. To what group of people did Huaman Poma belong? To whom did he write this letter?
   the Incas; King Philip III of Spain

2. According to Huaman Poma, what happened to Spanish officials once they left their ships?
   Possible answer: They immediately turned against the Indians.

4. According to Huaman Poma, what were the idols of the Spanish conquerors?
   gold, silver, and property

5. Why might Huaman Poma have written his letter?
   Possible answer: to persuade King Philip to exercise more control over his subjects

WORKSHEET
Chapter 25, Section 2

The Spanish Colonies

Write **T** if the statement if true and **F** if it is false. Rewrite each false statement to make it true.

1. __F__ The Council of the Indies, which was elected by the viceroys of New Spain and Peru, governed Spain's colonies in the New World from Mexico City.

2. __T__ Many of the Spaniards who served as government officials in Spain's colonies treated the Indians unfairly and enriched themselves at the expense of their Indian subjects.

3. __T__ American-born Spaniards resented the privileges given to the peninsulares and disliked having a lower social standing.

4. __F__ The Spanish followed a policy of religious tolerance similar to that followed in the English colonies of North America.

5. __F__ Mestizos often held positions as church officials or public administrators for the crown.

6. __F__ One's standing in Spanish colonial society was determined mostly by wealth.

7. __T__ In the 18th century, Spanish holdings in the New World were divided into and ruled as three regions.

8. __F__ Creoles, most of whom were of mixed Indian and Spanish heritage, had a lower social standing than mestizos, who were born in the colonies of Spanish parents.

1. Possible answer: The Council of the Indies was appointed by the Spanish king and met in Spain.

4. Possible answer: Spain allowed only Catholics to settle in its colonies. England allowed people of almost any religion to settle in its colonies.

5. Possible answer: Mestizos worked either as farmers on rented land or as shopkeepers, craftspeople, or soldiers.

6. Possible answer: One's standing in Spanish colonial society was determined by country of birth and ancestry.

8. Possible answer: Mestizos, most of whom were of mixed Indian and Spanish heritage, had a lower social standing than creoles, who were born in the colonies of Spanish parents.

WORKSHEET
Chapter 25, Section 3

Indians and Africans

Part A
Write the letter of each effect from the box beside its cause.

1. __c__ Making land in the colonies produce crops required a great deal of manual labor.

2. __f__ Official efforts to obtain better treatment for the Indians failed.

3. __h__ The Europeans brought many new diseases, such as smallpox, to the Americas.

4. __a__ Missionaries wanted to convert Indians in the New World to Catholicism.

5. __d__ Bartolomé de las Casas protested the cruel treatment of the Indians by the Spanish colonists.

6. __g__ The Spanish government suspected the Jesuit mission system of being a state within a state.

7. __i__ The Indian population was decimated by European diseases and overwork.

8. __b__ A shortage of Indian labor in Brazil left the coastal plantations without a sufficient work force.

9. __e__ Pierre Dominique Toussaint L'Ouverture led the revolt that freed slaves and established a new government.

a. Many Catholic missionaries came to the Spanish colonies.
b. The Portuguese government encouraged the African slave trade.
c. Finding a large, cheap labor force became the biggest problem facing the Spanish colonists.
d. Charles V of Spain chose a Spanish priest to be "Protector of the Indians."
e. Haiti became the first independent black nation in the Western Hemisphere.
f. Indians working on plantations and silver mines died by the thousands.
g. The Jesuits were ordered to leave Spanish America.
h. The greatest population disaster in recorded history occurred in Central and South America.
i. The Spanish government imported slaves from Africa to its colonies in America.

Part B
Write a paragraph that supports or provides details for the following statement:
Although the African slaves on the Brazilian plantations suffered from harsh working conditions, they were treated better than the slaves on Spanish Caribbean islands.

Example: The Portuguese looked upon Africans as people with souls, while the Caribbean plantation owners viewed the Africans as expendable property. Slaves in Brazil were converted to Christianity, and they attended church and took part in religious ceremonies. Some Brazilian slaves became skilled workers and craftspeople; some were taught to read and write. A few slaves bought their freedom or were freed when their masters died. All slaves in Brazil had a legal right to earn money and inherit land, unlike the slaves on the Spanish Caribbean islands.

WORKSHEET

Chapter 25, Section 4

Blend of Cultures in Latin America

Part A

For each statement below, write two or three sentences that support or provide details for that statement.

1. Slavery and racial prejudice did not prevent the mixing of and intermarriage between whites, blacks, and Indians in the Spanish and Portuguese colonies.
   Possible answer: Today 50 million Latin Americans are descended from African slaves. Much of the population in Mexico is a mixture of Spanish and Indian.

2. Spanish and Portuguese conquerors imposed their own beliefs and practices on the Indians.
   Possible answer: Spanish and Portuguese replaced Indian languages. Catholicism became the major religion from Mexico to Argentina.

3. Cities built by the colonists in Spanish America were influenced by Spanish city planning.
   Possible answer: Most cities were copied after Spanish cities. They had a central plaza in front of a large Catholic church and streets in squares around the central plaza.

4. Neither the Spanish nor the Portuguese considered women to be equal to men.
   Possible answer: Universities and colleges were attended mainly by men. Both the Spanish and Portuguese believed a woman's main role was to have children and to take care of the home.

Part B

The Spanish and Portuguese introduced many changes in technology, culture, and beliefs to the native people of the Americas. Which of these changes do you think had the most profound and long-lasting effect on the Indians' way of life? Explain your answer.
Example: The belief that Indians were inferior to Europeans led to the acquisition of Indian lands and the enslavement of Indians. It also placed the Indians at the bottom of Latin American society for hundreds of years.

_____

_____

_____

_____

WORKSHEET

Chapter 26, Section 1

The Enlightenment

In this worksheet you will review the ideas of the great thinkers and reformers of the Enlightenment.

Part A
Identify the philosophe most closely associated with each idea by writing **L** for Locke or **M** for Montesquieu. If neither philosophe would espouse the idea, write **X**.

1. __L__ The purpose of government is to protect people's rights to life, liberty, and property.

2. __M__ A rational society must contain many layers of social structures and governing bodies.

3. __L__ The agreement between people and their government is the "social contract."

4. __L__ If a government fails to protect a people's natural rights, then the people can set up a new government.

5. __X__ People are naturally wicked.

6. __X__ The best form of government is the absolute monarchy.

7. __M__ Liberty requires a separation and balance of powers in government.

Part B
Complete the chart.

Person	Significance
John Locke	**provided ideas on government theory for French and American philosophes, U.S. Declaration of Independence, and U.S. Constitution**
Montesquieu	**founded the scientific study of government and outlined the idea of separation and balance of power**
John Howard	**worked to improve prison conditions in England**
Jean Jacques Rousseau	**used idea of "noble savage" to reform education; stressed the power of the people in democracy**
Voltaire	**attacked superstition, intolerance, and lack of reason in society**
Denis Diderot	**helped to spread the new ideas of the Enlightenment through his encyclopedia**

WORSHEET
Chapter 26, Section 2
The Triumph of Parliament

In this worksheet you will review the English civil war and the emergence of a powerful English Parliament.

Part A
Number the events in the order in which they happened.

__7__ Parliament passed the English Bill of Rights.

__4__ The Restoration began.

__5__ Parliament passed the Habeas Corpus Act.

__8__ The last Stuart monarch in England died.

__6__ The Glorious Revolution brought William and Mary to the throne.

__1__ Charles I accepted the Petition of Right.

__3__ Oliver Cromwell became "Lord Protector" and ruled as a military dictator.

__2__ War broke out between the Cavaliers and Roundheads.

Part B
Write **C** next to each phrase that correctly completes the unfinished sentence.
(Each incomplete sentence may have more than one correct ending.)

1. After the death of Elizabeth I,

   __C__ James I became king.

   _____ the Hanoverian dynasty began.

   __C__ a conflict arose between the monarch and Parliament.

2. Because of his constant need of money, Charles I

   __C__ was forced to accept the Petition of Right.

   __C__ forced subjects to give loans to the government.

   _____ denied merchants seats in Parliament.

3. After the Roundheads defeated the Cavaliers,

   __C__ Charles I was beheaded.

   __C__ England became a military dictatorship.

   __C__ Parliament voted to abolish the monarchy.

   _____ Oliver Cromwell was exiled.

4. After the wife of James II bore a son,

   __C__ William of Orange invaded England.

   __C__ the Glorious Revolution occurred.

   __C__ the English feared they would have a long line of Catholic kings.

5. As a result of Charles I's entry into the House of Commons with a band of soldiers in 1642,

   _____ five Whigs were arrested.

   __C__ Charles fled to raise an army of supporters.

   __C__ a civil war began in England.

6. When George I became king of England,

   __C__ the Hanoverian dynasty began.

   __C__ a cabinet of members of Parliament was formed.

   __C__ the principal cabinet minister was chosen from the Whig party for nearly half a century.

WORKSHEET

Chapter 26, Section 3

In this worksheet you
will review events in
America immediately
before and after the War
of Independence.

The American War for Independence

Part A
Complete each statement with the explanations given in your text.

1. After 1763 England decided to enforce old revenue laws restricting the
colonies **because** Possible answer: England needed money to pay for debts incurred
by the French and Indian War.

2. The colonists vehemently opposed the Intolerable Acts **because** Possible answer: these acts closed Boston harbor and denied the
Massachusetts colonists the right to govern themselves.

3. Parliament had passed the Intolerable Acts **because** Possible answer: England had wanted to punish the colonists for the
Boston Tea Party.

4. The national government created by the Articles of Confederation can be
described as weak **because** Possible answer: the Articles left most political power in the hands
of the states.

5. Congress passed the Bill of Rights to amend the Constitution **because**
Possible answer: it wanted to reassure those who feared that a
strong central government would deny people civil liberties.

6. It may be said that the new American republic was not a full democracy **because**
Possible answer: only men with property, most of whom were white,
were permitted to vote.

Part B
Complete each analogy.

1. The idea of independence in the Declaration of Independence is to Locke as the
idea of checks and balances in the U.S. Constitution is to ___Montesquieu___.

2. The Articles of Confederation are to a weak national government as the
___U.S. Constitution___ is to a stronger national government.

3. The start of the American Revolution is to 1775 as the constitutional convention
is to ___1787___.

4. The U.S. Constitution is to checks and balances as the ___Bill of Rights___
is to protection of civil liberties.

WORKSHEET

Chapter 27, Section 1

Revolutionary Upheaval in France

In this worksheet you will trace events that caused the French Revolution or occurred during its upheaval.

Part A

Fill in the blanks with the words from the box that best complete the sentences.

Before the Revolution each French person belonged, by law, to one of three classes, or _____**estates**_____: the clergy belonged to the First Estate; the _____**nobility**_____ belonged to the Second Estate; and everyone else belonged to the Third Estate. Growing discontent among and within these classes was one factor leading to _____**revolution**_____ in France.

The government's _____**financial**_____ difficulty was another cause of the revolution. During the reign of Louis XVI, the French monarchy was close to _____**bankruptcy**_____, but laws exempted the First and Second estates from paying most _____**taxes**_____. To address the crisis Louis XVI was forced to share his power with the _____**Estates-General**_____, a legislative body. Since the Third Estate was not allowed to vote on an equal footing with the other two estates, the representatives from the Third Estate met separately and declared themselves to be a _____**National Assembly**_____.

bankruptcy	National Assembly	nobility	financial
estates	Estates-General	revolution	taxes

Part B

Number the events in the order in which they happened.

__3__ France becomes a constitutional monarchy.

__5__ Louis XVI is sentenced to death by the National Constitutional Convention.

__1__ Believing the Bastille to contain ammunition to be used against them, Parisian mobs storm that fort.

__4__ France's Legislative Assembly, fearing an attempt by Austria and Prussia to restore the French monarchy, declares war on them.

__7__ During rule by the Directory, political power resides in the upper middle class and former nobles.

__2__ In response to the violent uprisings by the peasants throughout France, the nobility and clergy relinquish many privileges that they had held since the feudal era.

__6__ Under Robespierre, the Committee of Public Safety embarks on the Reign of Terror.

WORKSHEET

Chapter 27, Section 2

In this worksheet you will review the rise and fall of Napoleon Bonaparte.

Napoleon in Power

Part A

Write **C** next to each phrase that correctly completes the unfinished sentence.
(Each sentence may have more than one correct ending.)

1. Determined to rule all of Europe, Napoleon I

   C was defeated at the battle of Trafalgar by a superior British navy.

   C controlled most of the European continent by 1806.

   _____ was outmaneuvered by the British, who established an international economic boycott against France.

   _____ was defeated by the Confederation of the Rhine.

2. Napoleon enacted significant reforms that

   _____ awarded special privileges to certain groups.

   C increased the strength and efficiency of the central government.

   _____ denied freedom of religion but guaranteed that the government would refrain from controlling the French Catholic Church.

   C modernized French law.

Part B

Present at least two specific facts from your text to support each statement.

1. Napoleon attempted to discipline the Iberian peninsula because of the smuggling operations conducted there.
   Possible answer: Napoleon invaded Portugal. He put his brother Joseph on the Spanish throne and stationed a French army in Spain.

2. Napoleon brought many ideals from the French Revolution to the conquered countries of Europe.
   Possible answer: Napoleon abolished feudalism and serfdom. He installed the Napoleonic Codes that emphasized equality before the law.

3. The sentiments of people in other countries began to turn against Napoleon during his economic boycott of British goods.
   Possible answer: People disliked the scarcity of goods. They began to develop patriotic feelings that incited them to turn against the French.

4. Napoleon's invasion of Russia in 1812 eventually led to his downfall.
   Possible answer: The Russian winter and "scorched earth" policy decimated the French army. This defeat inspired other nations to turn against Napoleon, causing his empire to collapse in 1814.

WORKSHEET
Chapter 27, Section 3

Latin American Revolutions

Part A
Write the correct name from the box that matches each description.

1. When he took control of Spain in 1808, Latin American colonists tried to break away from Spain.

2. After he was restored to the Spanish throne in 1814, he attempted to regain control of Spain's colonies.

3. Known as "the Liberator," he hoped to create a united states of Spanish America.

4. He was a creole soldier whose armies fought the Spanish in Argentina, Chile, and the city of Lima.

5. He launched the Mexican Revolution in 1810 by demanding independence from Spanish rule.

6. He was dictator of Mexico when it lost half of its territory to the United States in the Mexican War.

7. A mestizo army general, he set up a dictatorship that brought order and industry to Mexico.

8. In 1821 he became emperor of Brazil under a constitutional monarchy.

Napoleon

Ferdinand VII

Simón Bolívar

José de San Martín

Miguel Hidalgo

Santa Anna

Porfirio Díaz
Dom Pedro

Santa Anna	Ferdinand VII	Dom Pedro
Miguel Hidalgo	Napoleon	Porfirio Díaz
José de San Martín	Simón Bolívar	

Part B
Write a paragraph in which you explain the circumstances that led to the issuing of the Monroe Doctrine. How did European leaders react to the Doctrine?

Possible answer: After the French Revolution and the defeat of Napoleon, European leaders were alarmed by the spread of revolution in Latin America. They feared upheaval and hoped to promote stability by returning Latin America to its colonial status. To prevent European intervention in Latin America, U.S. President Monroe issued the Monroe Doctrine. European leaders knew that the powerful British navy would enforce the Monroe Doctrine and stayed out of Latin American affairs.

       © Scott, Foresman and Company

WORKSHEET
Chapter 27, Section 4

Influences of Two Revolutions

In this worksheet you will examine the impact of the American and French revolutions on the political and social ideas of other nations.

Part A
Write the name of the political concept from the box beside its example. (Not all names will be used.)

1. In the Pyrenees Mountains between France and Spain, a group of people known as the Basques work to create a separate nation for themselves.

2. In the United States, groups work to achieve the same rights enjoyed by other groups of citizens.

3. French and American revolutionary leaders claim that all people had the right to life, liberty, property, and the pursuit of happiness.

nationalism

equality

natural rights

equality	absolutism	natural rights
the Right	nationalism	male suffrage

Part B
For each statement below, write two or three sentences that support or provide details for that statement.

1. The French Revolution introduced a system of labeling political groups that remains in use today.
   Possible answer: The terms "Right" and "Left" designated conservative and liberal factions that sat on the right and left sides of the Assembly. The Right felt the revolution had gone far enough; the Left did not. Today, groups "on the right" want to maintain the status quo; "leftists" want political and social change.

2. The American and French revolutions provided precedents for peoples' right to overthrow repressive governments.
   Possible answer: The American Declaration of Independence and the French Declaration of the Rights of Man and of the Citizen established this right to rebel. People under oppressive governments throughout the world have followed the American and French examples.

3. The American and French revolutions enhanced the idea of nationalism.
   Possible answer: These revolutions led people to regard themselves as part of a nation, instead of subjects of a monarch. These revolutions reinforced the idea that a group of people had a right to form an independent nation.

Name   Date

WORKSHEET
Chapter 28, Section 1

In this worksheet you will review the factors that promoted the Industrial Revolution in Great Britain.

Industrialization in Britain

Part A
Write the letter of each effect from the box beside its cause.

1. __e__ The "enclosure acts" passed by Parliament between the 16th and 18th centuries allowed common lands to be fenced in.

2. __b__ An increased food supply, a decline in mortality rates, and an increase in birthrates contributed to Britain's huge population growth from the 16th to the 19th century.

3. __d__ Britain did not have a rigid class structure.

4. __a__ In 1733 John Kay invented the flying shuttle.

5. __c__ In 1735 Abraham Darby began to process iron ore with coke, or purified coal.

6. __f__ In the late 18th century, several engineers began to apply steam power to vehicles.

> a. Weaving time was cut in half.
> b. Britain's labor force increased.
> c. The iron industry moved from forest areas to coal regions.
> d. Clever but poor inventors and business people could improve themselves and their family's social position.
> e. Poor farmers became mobile wage earners, traveling to available jobs.
> f. The Rocket locomotive was invented in 1829, and in 1838 the *Sirius* crossed the Atlantic in record time.

Part B
For each statement below, write two or three sentences that support or provide details for that statement.

1. Britain's colonies contributed to its successful industrialization.
   Possible answer: The colonies provided raw materials for manufacture, such as wool and cotton. The growing population in the colonies increased the demand and the market for finished products. Parliament passed laws that forced colonists to buy manufactured goods from Britain.

2. In the 18th and 19th centuries, Britain's workplaces were transformed from rural cottage industries to small-town factories and urban factories.
   Possible answer: Before the Industrial Revolution, about half of Britain's products were made by workers at home from raw materials given to them by merchants. In the early 18th century, several inventions, such as the spinning mule, took workers out of their homes and into newly built factories near swift rivers, the sources of power. The invention of the steam engine in the early 19th century enabled factories to move away from the rivers and into cities.

© Scott, Foresman and Company

WORKSHEET
Chapter 28, Section 2

In this worksheet you
will study inventions
from the second
Industrial Revolution.

The Second Industrial Revolution

Part A
Use information from your text to write a brief description of the contributions of each
person listed below.

1. Henry Bessemer
   **Possible answer: Bessemer invented a process for making a good
   grade of steel in 1856.**

2. Michael Faraday
   **Possible answer: In 1831 Faraday showed how an electrical current
   could be made.**

3. Marie Curie
   **Possible answer: Curie, with her husband Pierre, discovered the
   element radium in 1898.**

Part B
Write **T** if the statement is true and **F** if it is false. On the lines below, rewrite each
false statement to make it true.

1. __F__ As the only industrialized nation in the 19th century, Britain thereby
   became the strongest nation in the world.

2. __T__ The second phase of industrialization included the use of many new
   technologies, especially in the development of steel, electricity, and chemicals.

3. __T__ When generated by water, electricity is clean, cheap, and almost without limit.

4. __F__ The work of scientists in the second half of the 19th century usually did
   not have much practical use.

5. __T__ Henry Ford was the first person to mass produce inexpensive automobiles.

**1. Possible answer: The Industrial Revolution spread quickly
from Britain to the European continent and the United States,
enabling other nations to challenge Britain's economic and
political supremacy.**

**4. Possible answer: During the 1800s the work of scientists helped
inventors and physicians create practical substances, such as
petroleum products, electric generators, and the smallpox vaccine.**

_____

_____

_____

WORKSHEET
Chapter 28, Section 3

Social Problems of Industrialism

In this worksheet you
will examine ideas about
the social problems
caused by urbanism and
industrialism.

Part A
In the blank before each statement, write the name of the person who might have said it.

1. The practice of laissez-faire will lead to a brutal society. Business people should cooperate with government and social leaders to create a society that provides the greatest happiness for the greatest number of people.

   Jeremy Bentham

2. The culprit of poverty in society is the incredible population growth, which will quickly outpace society's ability to supply food. To prevent horrible famines in the future, society's leaders must find ways to limit the population.

   Thomas Malthus

3. Literature can present, in powerful ways, the cruel results of the Industrial Revolution: poverty, hunger, and abusive labor practices against women and children. I condemn the brutal philosophy of Social Darwinism, which claims that the poor actually deserve their fate because they are inherently weak.

   Charles Dickens

4. In the past, nations incorrectly believed that they became wealthy by strictly controlling their economies. The way for a nation to become wealthy is to follow the motto "laissez-faire," or "let do." Government should keep out of economic matters and allow the laws of supply and demand to govern the economy. Workers' wages will then rise so that workers can buy more products, thus causing a greater demand.

   Adam Smith

Part B
Write the letter of the word or words from the box that best complete each sentence.

As industrialism grew, __c__ developed. Banks and financiers became important sources of __e__, and the __d__ was formed as a way to pool capital. In the late 19th century, financial organizations often joined together to form __a__, which held exclusive control of a commodity or service. By using large amounts of capital to swallow up other companies, such organizations tended to strangle __b__.

a. monopolies
b. competition
c. industrial capitalism
d. corporation
e. capital

WORKSHEET
Chapter 28, Section 4

Art and Thought

Part A
Fill in the blanks with the name or term that best completes each sentence.

1. As a reaction to the role that reason played during the Enlightenment, __romanticism__ emphasized those elements in life that could not be explained in rational terms alone.

2. The harsh social conditions of the 19th century were confronted and described in art and literature by the __realists__.

3. The French novelist Émile Zola, who belonged to the __naturalist__ group of writers, described life in the dispassionate way that a scientist would, without comment or feeling.

4. A Scottish socialist, __Robert Owen__, improved the lives of his factory employees, influencing those who later founded the cooperative movement.

5. As a way to build a better world for the working classes, the __socialists__ supported the idea that production and distribution should be controlled by the government, by associations of workers, or by the community as a whole.

6. In *Das Kapital*, __Karl Marx__ explained how the capitalist system works.

7. Karl Marx called the new lower class of workers, which had been created by industrialization, the __proletariat__.

8. According to Karl Marx, the process of __class struggle__ has been the cause of all important changes in history.

Part B
Write **C** next to each phrase that correctly completes the unfinished sentence.
(Each incomplete sentence may have more than one correct ending.)

1. The romanticists

   __C__ believed that primitive people were noble and good because civilization had not spoiled them.

   __C__ became interested in myths and fairy tales, such as those collected by the Grimm brothers.

   _____ were offended by Eugene Delacroix's use of color and exotic subject-matter.

   _____ embraced the crude and materialistic side of industrialization.

2. Realism and naturalism

   _____ were movements that led to the German theme of youthful geniuses who defied society's standards.

   _____ were movements that sought ways to escape from contemporary society.

   __C__ were movements that began as reactions to the sentimental ideals of romanticism.

   __C__ were movements that portrayed unpleasant conditions in a straightforward way.

WORKSHEET
Chapter 28, Section 5

In this worksheet you will examine some solutions to problems of urban, industrialized society.

Solutions to Industrial Problems

Part A
Indicate whether each of the following statements refers to Britain, Germany, or both by writing **B**, **G**, or both in the blank.

1. __B__ passed the Reform Bill of 1832 that took political power from agricultural regions and gave it to new industrial towns

2. __G__ established the Social Democratic Party

3. __G__ hoped to weaken socialism by passing laws to cure problems of urban industrial life

4. __B, G__ experienced long and bitter labor strikes in the 1880s and 1890s

5. __B__ mandated a national system of primary and secondary education in 1902

6. __B__ passed women's suffrage in 1918

7. __B, G__ had no sales or income tax in 1870

8. __B__ faced most of the issues of mass society and politics before other nations

Part B
Present at least two specific facts from your text to support each statement.

1. Not all nations allowed trade unions and social reforms.
   Possible answer: Autocratic governments of eastern Europe outlawed trade unions and had no orderly way to bring about reform.

2. In the 1830s the British industrialists gained power in Parliament at the expense of the upper-class landowners.
   Possible answer: The Reform Bill of 1832 gave seats in the House of Commons to northern industrial towns; in 1835 industrialists' power gained a hold on government, replacing the hold of the upper class.

3. Germany was the leader in social legislation beginning in the 1880s.
   Possible answer: The Germans passed laws in the 1880s to cure three main problems of urban industrialism: sickness, accident, and old age; later, workers received free medical care.

4. Some of the reforms in Europe in the 19th century were concerned with improving the lives of children.
   Possible answer: The labor reforms of 1833–1847 in Britain and the child labor laws of 1914 in Germany are examples of reforms that were concerned with child labor.

WORKSHEET
Chapter 29, Section 1

In this worksheet you will review European liberalism, nationalism, and reaction.

Liberalism, Nationalism, Revolution

Part A
Complete each statement with the explanations given in your text.

1. The leaders of the Great Powers felt that they had to put down revolutions in any European country **because**
   Possible answer: the revolutions threatened the stability of the entire continent.

2. A liberal revolution broke out in France under Charles X **because**
   Possible answer: the French people rejected his dissolution of the Chamber of Deputies after a large number of liberals won seats.

3. Belgian nationalists and middle-class liberals revolted in 1830 **because**
   Possible answer: they were unhappy with the arrangements of the Congress of Vienna and inspired by the success of French liberals.

4. In the 1830s the British reformed their voting laws and economic policies **because**
   Possible answer: liberals in Britain applied pressure for reform.

5. In the 1800s British working classes experienced extreme poverty **because**
   Possible answer: Great Britain retained its tariffs on imported grains, which kept the price of food high, and crop failures made food scarce.

6. Revolutions broke out in Europe in 1848 **because**
   Possible answer: the economic depression of the mid-1840s created conditions of unemployment, poverty, and instability.

Part B
Describe the main goals of the Congress of Vienna and the Concert of Europe.
Example: The peace talks of the Congress of Vienna were held to settle conflicts among the five strongest powers of Europe—Britain, France, Prussia, Austria, and Russia—and to strike a political balance among these powers. Austria, Russia, Prussia, and Britain—the Concert of Europe—agreed to meet periodically to guard the Vienna settlement and to keep peace in Europe.

_____

_____

_____

WORKSHEET
Chapter 29, Section 2

In this worksheet you will review the unification of Italy and Germany into national states.

The Unification of Italy and Germany

Part A
Number the events in each set in the order in which they happened.

Set 1

 2 Austria declared war on Italy.

 1 The Crimean War took place.

 4 The Kingdom of Italy was proclaimed.

 3 Most of northern Italy was united with Sardinia.

 5 Venetia and Rome came under Italian control, completing the unification of modern Italy.

Set 2

 5 The German Empire was formed.

 1 Otto von Bismarck became chancellor of Prussia.

 3 France declared war on Prussia.

 4 France was defeated by Prussia.

 2 Bismarck won wars against Denmark and Austria.

Part B
Identify the person described in each riddle.

1. I went to the Crimea to treat wounded soldiers in a war in which thousands of soldiers were needlessly wounded. I introduced modern nursing techniques that included rigid standards of cleanliness and effective organization. Who am I?

   Florence Nightingale

2. I led volunteer soldiers from all over Italy in the war against Austria. I urged my soldiers to continue fighting until all of Italy came under one Italian government. Who am I?

   Giuseppe Garibaldi

3. I was the chancellor of Prussia who believed strongly that Germany would not reach greatness through speeches and votes but "blood and iron." I led Prussia in victorious wars against Denmark, Austria, and France and am often credited with having brought about the unification of Germany. Who am I?

   Otto von Bismarck

4. As prime minister of Piedmont-Sardinia, I recognized that the only way to drive the Austrians from northern Italy was with the help of foreign powers. For that reason, I made a secret pact with Napoleon III at the Paris peace conference at the end of the Crimean War. My mastery of *realpolitik* paved the way for the eventual unification of Italy. Who am I?

   Camillo di Cavour

WORKSHEET

Chapter 29, Section 3

Democratic Gains in Western Europe

In this worksheet you will review democratic gains made between 1871 and 1914 in western Europe.

Part A

Write **T** if the statement is true and **F** if it is false. On the lines below, rewrite each false statement to make it true.

1. __F__ Under Benjamin Disraeli and William Gladstone, Britain took few steps to extend voting rights.

2. __T__ By 1891, Britain had established free and compulsory education.

3. __F__ Irish Catholics had won the right to form and run their own government by the mid-1800s.

4. __T__ Although Alfred Dreyfus was clearly a victim of anti-Semitism, the overthrowing of his conviction showed that in France the Republic was more powerful than the army.

5. __T__ Otto von Bismarck instituted Europe's first progressive program of social insurance in an attempt to attract workers away from socialism.

6. __F__ By 1890 the German emperors had had their fill of militaristic and nationalistic glory, and Wilhelm II decided to forego military and nationalist aims to pursue domestic reforms.

1. Possible answer: Under Disraeli and Gladstone, bills to extend voting rights were put forward; by 1884 all male adults in Britain had gained the right to vote.

3. Possible answer: Irish Catholics were denied Home Rule until 1914, when the Irish Free State was created.

6. Possible answer: Wilhelm II wanted to increase Germany's already considerable power by increasing militaristic and nationalistic spirit in the country.

Part B

Write the letter of the correct description or definition from the box beside its name.

1. __a__ Irish Free State
2. __d__ Ulster
3. __b__ anti-Semitism
4. __c__ Bundesrat
5. __e__ Chamber of Deputies and Senate
6. __g__ Whigs
7. __f__ Tories
8. __h__ Reichstag

a. southern Ireland
b. prejudice against Jews
c. upper house of German legislature
d. Northern Ireland
e. French legislature in Third Republic
f. Conservatives in England
g. Liberals in England
h. lower house of German legislature

WORKSHEET

Chapter 29, Section 4

Revolution and Reform

In this worksheet you will review reforms in non-industrial Europe and Russia.

Part A

Write the letter of the correct name or term from the box beside its definition or identifying phrase.

1. __e__ the 1825 attempt by intellectuals and army officers to overthrow the Russian government

2. __a__ the Russian tsar who, despite the liberal ideals of his youth, ruled as an autocrat from 1801 to 1825

3. __f__ act of 1861 that gave Russian serfs personal freedom and promised them land

4. __d__ region between Europe and Russia that was home to many Slavic ethnic groups who wanted independence

5. __b__ strict Russian tsar who ruled during the Crimean War, censored the press, took away academic freedoms, and sent enemies to Siberia

6. __g__ money paid by freed Russian serfs to former landlords for the use of the land

7. __c__ tsar who made reforms, including the abolishment of serfdom, in the hopes of strengthening Russia

a.	Alexander I
b.	Nicholas I
c.	Alexander II
d.	the Balkans
e.	Decembrist Revolt
f.	Edict of Emancipation
g.	redemption tax

Part B

Write the letter of each effect from the box beside its cause.

1. __c__ Russian intellectuals studied in France and learned democratic ideas; Russian army officers occupied France and were exposed to liberal ideas.

2. __f__ Idealistic Russians attempted to overthrow the government in the Decembrist Revolt.

3. __a__ The Russian army lost the Crimean War to the forces of more liberal societies.

4. __g__ Alexander II freed the serfs but did little to improve their living conditions.

5. __b__ Spain was defeated by the United States in the Spanish-American War of 1898.

6. __d__ Despite European assistance, the Turkish government remained corrupt and inefficient.

7. __e__ In the multi-ethnic Austrian-Hungarian Empire, Germans dominated in Austria, and Hungarians ruled in Hungary.

a.	Alexander II instituted the liberal reforms of the 1860s.
b.	Spain lost the remains of its once worldwide colonial empire.
c.	People returned to Russia eager to implement liberal changes in government and society.
d.	The Ottoman Empire disintegrated.
e.	Other ethnic groups in Austria-Hungary, such as the Czechs, Romanians, Slovaks, and Serbs, longed for self-rule.
f.	Tsar Nicholas I ruled Russia as a strict autocrat.
g.	The peasants could not support their families and remained in grinding poverty.

WORKSHEET
Chapter 29, Section 5
Advances in Democracy

Part A
Below are several statements of opinion. On the lines below each statement, write a statement of fact about the same subject.

1. All Canadians should speak only the English language.
   Possible answer: While the majority of Canadians speak English, a significant minority speak French; Canada is a bilingual nation.

2. The arrival of immigrants to the United States between 1790 and 1860 brought nothing but confusion to America.
   Possible answer: The arrival of immigrants to the United States provided needed laborers for a rapidly growing economy.

3. The process of industrializing America should have been delayed by 50 or 100 years to give people a chance to get used to territorial expansion.
   Possible answer: The process of industrializing America proceeded rapidly in the half-century after the Civil War.

4. During the 1860s the United States would have been better off allowing seceding states to leave the Union and begin their own independent nation.
   Possible answer: The United States government decided that no state could secede from the Union and went to war to defend that principle.

5. The only reason that the North won the Civil War was that it believed in doing the right thing.
   Possible answer: The North had these advantages in the Civil War: greater population, a highly developed industry, and wealth.

6. The United States, Canada, and Australia have nothing in common.
   Possible answer: These nations were once British colonies, officially use the English language, and have common political traditions.

Part B
Write a paragraph describing how democratic political rights were extended in the United States.
Possible answer: In the United States, Canada, and Australia, democratic political rights were extended from a narrow base of white, property-owning men to include all people. First, rights were broadened to include all white adult men, then to include men of other races. Finally, political rights were extended to women.

WORKSHEET
Chapter 30, Section 1

Imperialism in India

Part A
Write the letter of the identifying phrase from the box next to each item.

1. __e__ Bengal
2. __d__ sepoys
3. __c__ Muslim League
4. __a__ imperialism
5. __b__ Seven Years' War
6. __g__ India Act of 1784
7. __f__ Indian National Congress

a. the rule of one country over other countries or colonies
b. fought from 1756 to 1763; resulted in British control of Bengal
c. Muslim group working for self-government in India
d. Indian troops serving the British
e. a wealthy region in northeastern India during the 18th century
f. group of primarily Hindu leaders working for self-government in India
g. a British governmental action that limited the political power of the East India Company

Part B
Only three of the four items in each group are related in some way. Circle the item that does not belong and explain how the remaining three items are related.

1. British East India Company   French East India Company   Mughal rulers   (sepoys)
   Possible answer: As their hold over India weakened, Mughal rulers gave the British East India Company and the French East India Company opportunity to operate in India.

2. representative self-government   Indian National Congress   (Mughal Empire) Muslim League
   Possible answer: The Indian National Congress and the Muslim League were organizations that worked for Indian representative self-government.

Part C
Write a paragraph describing the results of the British administration of India.
Possible answer: On the positive side, the British unified much of the subcontinent under one government and one language. They suppressed crime and outlawed two practices which were harmful to Indian women (suttee and the killing of infant girls). They also improved Indian medicine, transportation, communication, and irrigation. On the negative side, rapid population growth resulted in a declining living standard and widespread poverty. The British also interfered with India's traditional economy by introducing cheap textiles.

WORKSHEET
Chapter 30, Section 2

In this worksheet you will review imperialism Asia.

Imperialism in Asia

Part A
Complete each analogy.

1. The Opium War was to Britain as the Sino-Japanese War was
   to _____**Japan**_____.

2. Formosa in 1895 was to Japan as _____**Hong Kong**_____ in 1842 was
   to Britain.

3. Spheres of interest were to trade and economic rights as _____**extraterritoriality**_____
   was to trial rights.

4. The Treaty of Kanagawa was to Japanese-U.S. relations as the
   _____**Treaty of Nanking**_____ was to Chinese-British relations.

5. Liaotung peninsula was to Japan and Russia as the opium trade was
   to _____**Britain**_____ and _____**China**_____.

Part B
For each pair of items, write a sentence that clearly explains the relationship
between the two.

1. Japan/imperialism
   **Possible answer: Japan resisted takeover by imperialist power and
   eventually practiced imperialism itself.**

2. concessions/extraterritoriality
   **Possible answer: Foreigners enjoyed the right of extraterritoriality as
   part of concessions granted to them by the Chinese government.**

3. Meiji Era/Western models
   **Possible answer: During the Meiji Era, Japan patterned itself after
   Western models in constitution, military, and industry.**

4. "mixed" system/Japanese economy
   **The Japanese economy developed as a "mixed" system, one allowing
   both private and government enterprise.**

5. Japanese imperialism/imports and export markets
   **Motives for the development of Japanese imperialism included
   Japan's need to import food and raw materials, as well as its desire
   for export markets for its manufactured goods.**

WORKSHEET

Chapter 30, Section 3

In this worksheet you will review imperialism in Asia and the Pacific.

Imperialism in Asia and the Pacific

Part A
Write the name of the imperialist nation that is associated with each set of clues below.
(Some names of nations may be used more than once.)

1. Black Sea, Persian Gulf, Pacific Ocean, warm water ports _____**Russia**_____

2. Hawaii, Guam, Philippines, Samoa _____**United States**_____

3. Vladivostok, Trans-Siberian Railroad, northern Persia _____**Russia**_____

4. Saigon, Indochina, Tahiti, New Caledonia _____**France**_____

5. Cochin-China, Cambodia, Annam, Laos _____**France**_____

6. southern Persia, Burma, Ceylon, Singapore _____**Britain**_____

7. East Indies, instruction in native languages _____**Netherlands**_____

8. Australia, New Zealand, Fiji _____**Britain**_____

Part B
Read Rudyard Kipling's poem "The White Man's Burden" that appears in Section 3 of your text, and answer the questions that follow.

1. Summarize Kipling's ideas of the imperialists' duties towards conquered peoples.
   Possible answer: It is the duty of white people to send their best to bring civilization to the less fortunate. Even though these peoples may resist, the colonizer must continue to serve their need for civilization.

2. Why might people in the colonies object to this poem?
   Possible answer: The poem implies that European culture is superior to those of the conquered peoples. It portrays the task of "civilizing" these peoples as a burden and uses derogatory terms to describe native, child-like people. The poem fails to reflect appreciation for the rich cultures of Africa and Asia.

3. The imperialist powers gained for themselves economic advantages not mentioned in Kipling's poem. Use information from your text to write a paragraph describing these advantages.
   Example: The Dutch reaped handsome profits from its colony's raw materials. Russia acquired a warm water port, Britain obtained refueling stations, and the United States gained a thriving export trade in the Hawaiian Islands.

WORKSHEET

Chapter 30, Section 4

In this worksheet you will review the European colonization of Africa.

Africa Under European Control

Part A
Present at least one specific fact from your text to support each statement.

1. British and French interests in North Africa caused conflict between the two countries.
   Possible answer: The Fashoda incident, in which French and British troops collided, almost led to a war between the two countries in 1898.

2. The International Congo Association was able to acquire much African land.
   Possible answer: Henry Stanley gained huge tracts of land by making more than 400 treaties with African chiefs.

3. Abyssinia, later known as Ethiopia, was the exception to the pattern of European colonization.
   Possible answer: Ethiopia retained its independence after it successfully repelled Italian invaders in 1896; it was one of only two African countries to resist European imperialism.

4. In some respects European rule improved living conditions in Africa.
   Possible answer: The Europeans ended slavery and ethnic warfare in some areas; they built roads, cities, and industries and attempted to improve educational and health standards.

5. Africans suffered greatly at the hands of the European colonizers.
   Possible answer: Many Europeans cruelly exploited Africans by uprooting them from their homes, exacting forced labor and heavy taxes from them, and inflicting severe punishments.

Part B
Identify the European colonial power described by each phrase. Write **BR** for Britain, **F** for France, or **BE** for Belgium. A phrase may describe more than one colonial power.

1. ___**F**___ invaded Algeria in 1830
2. ___**BR, F**___ extended influence into North Africa
3. ___**F**___ dreamed of an empire from Dakar to Djibouti
4. ___**BR**___ made Egypt a protectorate
5. ___**BE**___ funded Stanley's International Congo Association
6. ___**BR**___ founded a condominium in the Sudan

WORKSHEET

Chapter 30, Section 5

Intervention in Latin America

Read the statements below and write **F** for fact and **O** for opinion before each one. For each opinion, explain on the lines below one other point of view that people might hold.

1. **O** Dollar diplomacy was actually a form of economic exploitation of poorer nations by richer nations.

2. **F** After the Spanish-American War, Cuba became in effect a protectorate of the United States.

3. **O** The United States intervened in the Dominican Republic on highly questionable grounds.

4. **F** During the period 1880–1910, Latin American governments tended to be very unstable, experiencing frequent revolutions and changes of rulers.

5. **F** The United States had the support of the British navy in its enforcement of the Monroe Doctrine.

6. **O** Spain was responsible for the outbreak of the Spanish-American War because it sank the *Maine* in Havana harbor.

7. **F** The United States gained Puerto Rico, Guam, and the Philippines as a result of its victory in the Spanish-American War.

8. **O** U.S. intervention in Latin America was necessary to maintatin political stability in the Western Hemisphere.

1. Possible answer: Dollar diplomacy worked to the mutual advantage of both rich and poor nations by promoting the economic development of undeveloped areas.

3. Possible answer: The United States' intervention was justified because the Dominican Republic's inability to repay its creditors invited foreign intervention.

6. Possible answer: No one knows for certain who was responsible for the sinking of the *Maine*.

8. Possible answer: U.S. intervention in Latin America at times created instability in the Western Hemisphere and led to Latin American resentment of the United States.

WORKSHEET
Chapter 31, Section 1

In this worksheet you will review facts about events that led to World War I.

The European Alliance System

Part A
Choose words from the box to complete the chart. Names of some countries will be used several times.

Name of Alliance	Date	Participating Countries
Dual Alliance	1879–1918	Germany, Austria
Triple Alliance	1882	Italy, Germany, Austria
Reinsurance Treaty	1887	Germany, Russia
Entente Cordiale	1904	Britain, France
Triple Entente	1907	Russia, France, Britain

Reinsurance Treaty	1887	Russia	1882
Germany	*Entente Cordiale*	Britain	Italy
Austria	France	1907	Dual Alliance

Part B
Write **C** next to each phrase that correctly completes the unfinished sentence. (Each incomplete sentence may have more than one correct ending.)

1. Britain viewed Germany as a threat because of

   a. __C__ Germany's attempts to build a strong navy.

   b. _____ Germany's role in the Russo-Japanese War.

   c. __C__ competition for economic markets.

   d. __C__ competition for colonies.

2. Britain viewed Russia as a threat because

   a. __C__ both competed for territories in Asia.

   b. __C__ Russia won the Russo-Turkish war.

   c. __C__ Russia had a chance to become a sea power in the Mediterranean.

   d. _____ Russia boycotted the Congress of Berlin.

3. Some of the factors that caused World War I were

   a. __C__ industrialization.

   b. __C__ nationalism.

   c. __C__ competition.

   d. _____ agricultural growth.

WORKSHEET

Chapter 31, Section 2

In this worksheet you will review the functions of some pre-World War I international agencies.

Early International Organizations

Part A
Present at least two specific facts from your text to support each statement.

1. The world economy needed peace.
   Possible answer: In peacetime raw materials and finished goods could be sold worldwide and businesses could operate everywhere without danger. War would destroy the prosperity that came from international trade.

2. Some positive forces favored peace.
   Possible answer: Many business and political leaders worked for world harmony. International organizations such as the International Telegraph Union and General Postal Union were set up to improve worldwide communication. The Olympic games were revived, bringing together diverse people.

Part B
Write the correct name to match each description.

1. concerned with humane treatment of wounded persons, prisoners, and civilians during wartime
   Geneva Convention

2. established to improve rapid worldwide communication
   International Telegraph Union

3. set up to encourage cooperation and promote trade among American nations
   Pan American Union

4. formed to improve international mail service
   General Postal Union

5. founded to help lessen hardships of war
   International Red Cross

WORKSHEET
Chapter 31, Section 3

In this worksheet you will review events relating to the escalation of the Balkan crisis.

The Escalation of the Balkan Crisis

Part A
Number the events in the order in which they happened.

__2__ Count Berchtold asked Germany to help stop Serbian agitation.

__5__ With French support assured, the Russian army mobilized its forces.

__8__ Despite Belgian neutrality, German troops entered Belgium.

__1__ Archduke Francis Ferdinand and his wife were killed.

__6__ Germany demanded that Russia halt its war moves and that France remain neutral.

__3__ Count Berchtold sent an ultimatum to Serbia.

__9__ Britain declared war on Germany.

__7__ Germany declared war on France.

__4__ Austria declared war on Serbia.

Part B
Use information from the text to complete each of the following statements.

1. The Balkans were known as "the powder keg of Europe" **because**
   Possible answer: tensions there threatened to ignite a major war.

2. Austria did not want the unification of the Serbs **because**
   Possible answer: it feared that unification would cause other minority Slavic groups to demand self-rule.

3. Kaiser Wilhelm II promised support to Austria **because**
   Possible answer: he wanted to keep Austria as an ally and he believed that the conflict could be kept within the Balkans.

4. Berchtold believed that other countries would be afraid to help Serbia **because**
   Possible answer: Germany was a strong country and an Austrian ally.

5. The Russians wanted to help the Serbs **because**
   Possible answer: they were fellow Slavs and believed that a Serbian defeat would be a major blow to Russia's standing.

6. Germany declared war on France **because**
   Possible answer: Russia refused to halt war moves and France refused to remain neutral.

WORKSHEET
Chapter 31, Section 4

A Look at World War I

In this worksheet you
will review the major
developments of
World War I.

Part A

In the blank before each item below, write the letter from the time line that matches
the date of the item. Some letters will be used twice.

A	B	C	D	E
1914	1915	1916	1917	1918

1. **B** The Armenian Massacre occurred.
2. **A** Japan joined the Allies.
3. **E** World War I ended on November 11.
4. **B** Italy joined the Allies.
5. **A** The Ottoman Empire joined the Central Powers.
6. **E** Russia and Germany signed the Treaty of Brest-Litovsk.
7. **D** China declared war against Germany and Austria.
8. **D** The United States joined the Allies.

Part B

Use information from your text to explain the significance of the following in
World War I.

1. trench warfare
   **Possible answer: Trench warfare was used on the western front.
   Enemy machine guns firing from trenches could wipe out line after
   line of attacking soldiers. Although fierce battles were fought and
   many soldiers were killed, very little territory changed hands.**

2. a two-front war
   **Possible answer: German troops had to fight on the western front
   against the Allies and on the eastern front against the Russians. This
   division of effort sapped Germany's effectiveness on both fronts.**

3. Treaty of Brest-Litovsk
   **Possible answer: Under terms of this treaty, Russia lost one-third of
   its people, nine-tenths of its coal mines, and all of its oil fields;
   Germany increased its power tremendously and, with the eastern front
   secure, moved all of its troops to the western front.**

WORKSHEET
Chapter 31, Section 5

In this worksheet you will review changes made to the map of Europe as a result of World War I.

Changes in Europe's Boundaries

Use information from the two maps below and from your text to answer the questions.

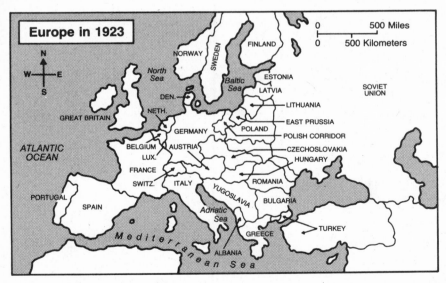

1. What new nations were created from the old Russian Empire?
Estonia, Latvia, Lithuania, Finland, and Poland

2. What nations disappeared altogether?
Serbia; Montenegro; Austria-Hungary; Ottoman, German empires

3. What new nation was created along the Adriatic Sea?
Yugoslavia

WORKSHEET

Chapter 32, Section 1

In this worksheet you will review events leading to collapse of the tsarist regime in Russia.

The Collapse of Tsarist Rule

Part A
Write the letter of the term from the box next to its definition or identifying phrase.

1. __c__ council of workers
2. __g__ national parliament created by the constitution of 1905
3. __e__ massacre of unarmed workers by the tsar's troops in 1905
4. __a__ class of educated people in Russia
5. __f__ policy requiring that non-Russians use Russian language in public life
6. __d__ mob attack against Jewish enclaves in Russia
7. __h__ humiliating defeat for Russian imperialism
8. __b__ radical Marxist group formed by Vladimir Ilyich Lenin

a. intelligentsia
b. Bolshevik party
c. soviet
d. pogrom
e. "Bloody Sunday"
f. "russification"
g. Duma
h. Russo-Japanese War

Part B
Write **C** next to each phrase that correctly completes the unfinished sentences.
(Each incomplete sentence may have more than one correct ending.)

1. Actions of the last two tsars included
   __C__ tightening of censorship.
   __C__ religious persecution.
   __C__ banning of all political parties.
   __C__ brutal suppression of striking workers.
   __C__ land reform.

2. Alexander Kerensky's Provisional Government failed to win popular support because it
   ____ supported the peasants in their seizure of estates.
   __C__ refused to carry out land reforms.
   __C__ continued Russian involvement in World War I.
   __C__ could not restore order in face of chaotic conditions.
   __C__ delayed free elections.

3. The constitution established in 1905
   ____ set up the soviets.
   __C__ set up trade unions.
   __C__ legalized political parties.
   ____ enabled reforms to take place over the tsar's objections.
   __C__ established the Duma.

4. Alexander II's refusal to establish a national assembly led
   __C__ some people to conclude that the tsarist government must be overthrown.
   __C__ some intelligentsia to embrace radicalism.
   ____ to the establishment of legal political parties.
   __C__ to the formation of secret terrorist organizations.

© Scott, Foresman and Company

WORKSHEET
Chapter 32, Section 2

The Bolshevik Revolution

In this worksheet you
will review the process
by which the Bolsheviks
took control of Russia.

Part A
Write **T** if the statement if true and **F** if its is false. On the lines below, rewrite each
false statement to make it true.

1. __T__ In order to transform Russia into a communist society, all private
property was taken over by the state.

2. __T__ Lenin believed that force was necessary to abolish capitalism and
establish a classless society.

3. __F__ Lenin's establishment of a communist dictatorship helped end the
civil war.

4. __F__ The Allies sent troops to help overthrow the "Reds" because they wanted
Russia to end its war with Germany.

5. __F__ Even after World War I, the Allies tried to undermine the communists
because they wanted to punish Lenin for his alliance with Germany.

6. __T__ The communists finally won the civil war because they had a superior
army and because the Russian people resented the Allied intervention.

**3. Possible answer: Lenin's attempt to establish a communist
dictatorship was opposed by many Russians, from socialists to
monarchists, and led to civil war.**

**4. Possible answer: The Allies sent troops to help overthrow the "Reds"
because they wanted to bring Russia back into the war against
Germany and because they wanted to destroy Lenin's regime.**

**5. Possible answer: Even after World War I, the Allies tried to help bring
down the communists, because they feared communism would
spread to the rest of Europe.**

Part B
Underline the term in parentheses that correctly completes each sentence.

1. After many long years of war, the communist government in 1921

   (<u>did</u>/refused to) retreat from war communism.

2. Under the New Economic Policy, the state owned basic industries, and private

   enterprise in retail trade (<u>was</u>/was not) allowed.

3. Trotsky (<u>supported</u>/did not support) the idea of a socialist world revolution.

4. Stalin believed that the world revolution (<u>would</u>/would not) spread to other

   countries if the Soviet Union first developed its own socialism.

5. In 1925 Stalin's policy (<u>was</u>/was not) accepted at the 14th Party Congress.

WORKSHEET
Chapter 32, Section 3

The "Stalinization" of the Soviet Union

Part A
Complete the chart with information from Section 3 of your text.

Stalin's Action	Purpose of Action
Collectivization of agriculture	To promote greater efficiency in food production
Forced export of foodstuffs	**To raise money for industrialization**
Exile of some peasants to barren regions	**To crush opposition to collectivization among uncooperative peasants**
Abandonment of motto "to each according to his needs"	**To reward those in occupations deemed valuable to the state**
Purges and public trials	**To consolidate Stalin's absolute power**

Part B
Describe how "Stalinization" affected each of the following aspects of Soviet life.

1. economic development
   Possible answer: Industrialization was achieved in 12 years. Unemployment was almost wiped out.

2. civil liberties
   Possible answer: Although women gained legal equality with men, there was little individual freedom.

3. standard of living
   Possible answer: Wider employment, medical care, and old-age pensions and insurance improved the lives of ordinary Soviet citizens.

4. artistic freedom
   Possible answer: Since artists were expected to create works supporting the government, innovation and imagination suffered.

WORKSHEET
Chapter 32, Section 4

In this worksheet you will review the Soviet Union's relations with other countries.

Soviet Foreign Policy Before 1939

Part A
Number the events in the order in which they happened.

___4___ The Soviet Union is admitted to the League of Nations.

___5___ The Soviet Union aids anti-Franco forces in the Spanish Civil War.

___1___ Germany and the Soviet Union sign the Treaty of Rapallo.

___6___ The Soviets negotiate a non-aggression pact with Germany.

___2___ France and England formally recognize the Soviet Union.

___3___ The United States formally recognizes the Soviet Union.

Part B
Write the letter of each effect from the box beside its cause.

1. ___d___ Nazi promotion of anticommunist feeling

2. ___c___ formation of communist parties in most countries of the world

3. ___b___ 1922 Soviet-German treaty

4. ___e___ formation of Popular Front policy

5. ___a___ Chinese fear of communist control in 1927

> a. Chinese rejection of Soviet help to unify China
> b. closer ties between two "outcast" nations
> c. an association of communist parties called the Comintern
> d. Stalin's adoption of collective security policy
> e. decreased emphasis on world revolution; increased support to nations struggling against dictatorships

Part C
Agree or disagree with the following statement: Stalin reversed his foreign policy objectives several times during the 1920s and 1930s. Explain your reasoning.

Students who agree should point out that Stalin was pro-German at first (1922), then anti-German (1934–1939), and then once again pro-German (1939). His views toward working with the Western democracies also vacillated. Students who disagree should observe that Stalin's foreign policy objectives remained consistent—to find any ally to ensure Soviet security and survival. Stalin sought friends wherever and whenever he could find them: Germany when both were considered outcast nations; the Western democracies when both shared a fear of Nazi aggression; and Germany again when neither Britain nor France showed willingness to help the Soviet Union.

WORKSHEET
Chapter 33, Section 1

In this worksheet you will review the nationalist movement in China.

Chinese Nationalism

Part A
Write the letter of each term or name from the box next to its identifying phrase.

1. __f__ people who share a common history, language, and culture
2. __e__ the desire for national independence and a strong national government
3. __d__ special political and economic privileges granted to European nations in China
4. __b__ the author of *Three Principles of the People*, which called for China's freedom from foreign control
5. __a__ the Nationalist party leader who ordered an attack on Chinese Communists
6. __h__ the Chinese Communists' 6,000-mile retreat to Yanan after their defeat by the Nationalist army.
7. __g__ the Nationalist People's Party
8. __c__ the Chinese Communist leader

a. Chiang Kai-shek	**c.** Mao Zedong	**e.** nationalism	**g.** Guomindang
b. Sun Yat-sen	**d.** spheres of influence	**f.** national group	**h.** the Long March

Part B
Write a brief answer to each of the following questions.

1. If you were Sun Yat-sen in 1910, what would you want most for China?
   Example: the overthrow of the Manchu dynasty

2. If you were Sun Yat-sen in the 1920s, what would be your greatest hope for your country?
   Example: the unification of China under the Guomindang government

3. If you were Chiang Kai-shek in the 1930s, what changes might you make in response to the common Chinese resentment of foreigners?
   Example: eliminate foreigners' special trading rights and territory

4. If you were Mao Zedong in retreat after the Long March, what might be your plans for the future?
   Example: winning peasant support, continuing civil war

5. If you were either a Communist or a Nationalist Chinese in 1937, how might you feel about the newly formed alliance with your political foe?
   Example: willingness to trust new ally; continued suspicion of ally

WORKSHEET
Chapter 33, Section 2

In this worksheet you will review Gandhi's campaign for independence in India.

Indian Independence Movement

Part A
Complete each statement with the explanations given in your text.

1. Many Indians loyally supported the British war effort during World War I **because**
   Possible answer: they hoped that the British would reward their loyalty with self-government after the war.

2. Gandhi opposed the Government of India Act of 1919 **because**
   Possible answer: the act did not grant the Indian government complete independence.

3. The British eventually consented to give India independence **because**
   Possible answer: Gandhi's campaign against the British was so effective.

4. During the 1930s the British met with Indian leaders **because**
   Possible answer: the British wanted to prepare India gradually for self-government.

5. Full independence for India was not granted until 1947 **because**
   Possible answer: World War II broke out before the independence-giving process had been completed.

Part B
During the Amritsar massacre, British soldiers opened fire on unarmed Indian demonstrators assembled in an open space surrounded by brick houses and a high wall. Write an editorial for an Indian newspaper denouncing the massacre but maintaining the principles of nonviolent resistance.
Students' answers may urge Indians not to answer violence with violence but to rise above vengeance. Editorials may urge readers to use their grief and anger to give them strength to practice civil disobedience and noncooperation.

WORKSHEET

Chapter 33, Section 3

Nationalism in the Middle East

In this worksheet you will review the Balfour Declaration and other important events promoting nationalism in the Middle East.

Part A

Write the letter of each phrase from the box next to the name of the country it identifies.
A country may have more than one identifying phrase

1. __e, a__ Egypt
2. __d__ Palestine
3. __h, f__ Turkey
4. __b, g__ Saudi Arabia
5. __i, c__ Iran

> **a.** country adjacent to the Suez Canal
> **b.** Ibn-Saud's kingdom
> **c.** Reza Shah Pahlavi's kingdom
> **d.** the geographical focus of the Balfour Declaration
> **e.** British protectorate that revolted
> **f.** former home to 1.4 million Greeks
> **g.** location of rich oil reserves
> **h.** Kemal Atatürk's republic
> **i.** a Muslim but not an Arab land

Part B

The Balfour Declaration was a letter written in 1917 by the British foreign secretary, Arthur James Balfour, to a leading British Zionist, Lord Rothschild. The wording and intent of the document have been the subject of much debate. Read the following quotation from the Balfour Declaration and answer the questions below.

His Majesty's Government views with favour the establishment in Palestine of a National Home for the Jewish people, and will use their best endeavours to facilitate the achievement of this object, it being clearly understood that nothing shall be done which may prejudice the civil and religious rights of existing non-Jewish communities in Palestine, or the rights and political status enjoyed by Jews in any other country.

1. Where did the British government propose to establish a homeland for Jews? What group of people in the same place does the declaration seek to protect?
   Palestine. The declaration seeks to protect non-Jews living in Palestinian communities.

2. How might the British goals identified in question 1 be viewed as incompatible?
   Possible answer: To settle Jews in Palestine might result in a loss of land and political power for non-Jewish groups; some might view these losses as "prejudicing" the rights of non-Jewish residents.

3. Why has this document been considered so controversial?
   Possible answer: Palestine was not yet a British mandate at the time the letter was written, and Arabs made up the larger part of the population in Palestine.

WORKSHEET
Chapter 33, Section 4

Fascist Dictatorships

Part A
For each statement below, write two or three sentences that support or provide details for that statement.

1. The communist and fascist dictatorships that arose after World War I curtailed individual liberties in similar ways.
   Possible answer: Neither communism nor fascism permitted opposing political parties to exist. Both used censorship, denied civil rights, and assumed comprehensive control of people's lives.

2. Fear of communism created Italian popular support for the Fascist party.
   Possible answer: Post-World War I economic problems led Marxist workers to strike. The strikes frightened middle-class Italians, who feared a communist revolution, into supporting the Fascists.

3. The Third Reich was a totalitarian state.
   Possible answer: A totalitarian state is one in which the government has total control of every area of life. The Third Reich controlled the German economy, schools, unions, newspapers, radio, and films.

4. The Nazis systematically eliminated Jews from German national life.
   Possible answer: The 1935 Nuremberg Laws took citizenship rights from Jews and forbade intermarriage. The government took away the Jews' property and forced Jews to live in ghettoes.

Part B
Number the events in the order in which they happened.

___2___ The Italian king invited Mussolini to become prime minister.

___4___ A strong military clique gained power in Japan.

___1___ The Weimar Republic was established in Germany.

___3___ Hitler tried to seize power in Bavaria in the Beer Hall Putsch.

___5___ Hitler became chancellor of the Third Reich.

___7___ The Nuremberg Laws were passed.

___6___ Hitler became Führer of Germany.

WORKSHEET

Chapter 34, Section 1

In this worksheet you will review some of the economic problems that led to world depression.

Causes of the World Depression

From the box below the diagrams, select the terms or phrases that best complete the missing parts of each chain. Use your completed diagrams to complete the following exercise.

Causes of the Great Depression

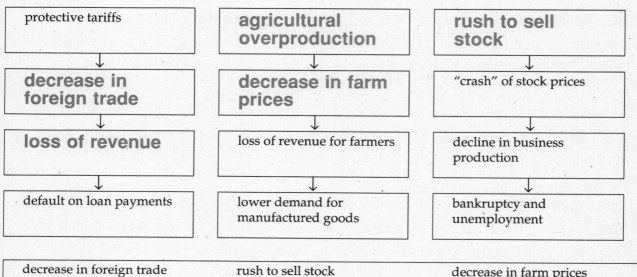

1. According to the chart, what was the immediate cause of the "crash" of stock prices?
   Possible answer: Everybody rushed to sell stock; there were no buyers, causing prices to fall drastically.

2. Explain how a protective tariff—intended to protect a nation's producers—can sometimes cause producers to lose revenue.
   Possible answer: A tariff can cut off markets for a producer's goods, leading to a loss of revenue.

3. Explain how a highly productive farm harvest could lead to lower, rather than higher, farm income.
   Possible answer: Overproduction could lead to a surplus and lower farm prices. Lower prices could lead to lower farm income.

4. Explain how farmers' problems also hurt manufacturers during the world depression.
   Possible answer: Since the farmers had less money, they could not purchase a high volume of manufactured goods.

WORKSHEET
Chapter 34, Section 2

Toward World War II

In this worksheet you will review events leading to the outbreak of World War II.

Part A

For each set, number the events in the order in which they happened.

1. __3__ Germany attacked Austria.
   __2__ The Rome-Berlin Axis was formed.
   __4__ Japan joined Germany and Italy in alliance.
   __1__ Hitler came to power in Germany.

2. __2__ The League of Nations condemned Japan.
   __1__ Japan seized several provinces in Manchuria.
   __4__ The Chinese set up a new capital at Chongqing.
   __3__ Japan launched a full-scale war against China.

3. __2__ The Spanish set up a republic.
   __3__ The Spanish Civil War began.
   __1__ King Alfonso III of Spain was forced to abdicate.
   __4__ The Loyalists were defeated.

4. __1__ Stalin signed a pact with Hitler.
   __3__ Britain and France declared war on Germany.
   __4__ The Rome-Berlin-Tokyo Axis was formed.
   __2__ Germany attacked Poland.

Part B

Use the following statistics to complete the bar graph showing the expansion of Germany. (For each bar you will have to add the area of the new territory to that previously annexed or seized.)

a. German territory, 1919	101,500 square miles
b. annexation of Austria, March, 1938	+ 32,400 square miles
c. annexation of the Sudetenland, Oct., 1938	+ 10,800 square miles
d. seizure of Czechoslovakia, March, 1939	+ 35,300 square miles
e. seizure of Polish Corridor, March, 1939	+ 1,100 square miles

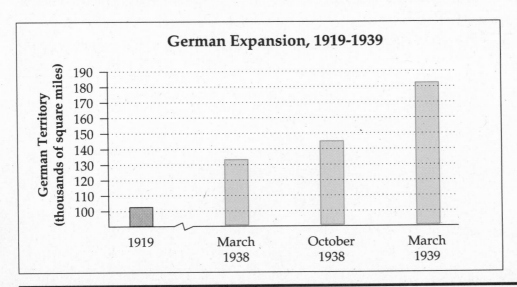

German Expansion, 1919-1939

WORKSHEET

Chapter 34, Section 3

World War II: The Dark Years

Part A

Support each statement with at least one specific example from your text.

1. World War II was more a global war than World War I had been.
   Possible answer: Fighting took place in Europe, the Pacific, Asia, and North Africa.

2. Poland had little chance against the invading German army.
   Possible answer: The Polish air force was destroyed on the ground. The Polish cavalry charged against mighty German tanks.

3. The battle of Britain was a turning point in the war.
   Possible answer: When Germany was unable to defeat England, other countries saw that the Nazi war machine could be stopped.

4. President Roosevelt's decision to establish "relocation centers" for Japanese Americans remains controversial.
   Possible answer: Many people doubt whether this violation of civil liberties could be justified. Others view the action as a reasonable war measure.

5. The American conversion to a war economy was one of the wonders of the industrial world.
   Possible answer: The United States soon began to supply Britain and the Soviet Union with the arms and equipment needed to halt the Axis. A plant near Detroit finished a B-24 bomber every 63 minutes.

Part B

Identify the country described by each phrase by writing **B** for Britain, **J** for Japan, **US** for the United States, **G** for Germany, and **USSR** for the Soviet Union.

USSR attacked Finland

US was isolationist for first two years of the war

G broke a 1939 pact with the Soviet Union

J planned to build an empire in Southeast Asia

B was called by Hitler "a nation of shopkeepers"

G was known for its *blitzkrieg*

B inspired captive people everywhere by successfully resisting Hitler

US entered the war after a surprise attack on a Pacific naval base

WORKSHEET
Chapter 34, Section 4

In this worksheet you
will review events of
the height and the end
of World War II.

The Height and End of World War II

Part A
Complete each analogy.

1. El Alamein is to North Africa as Midway is to the _____.
North Pacific

2. The battle for Stalingrad is to the eastern front as the _____ is to the western front.
invasion of Normandy

3. Casablanca is to war strategy as _____ is to peace terms.
Yalta

4. General Douglas MacArthur is to "island-hopping" as _____ is to "Operation Overlord."
General Dwight D. Eisenhower

5. The "New Order" is to economic exploitation as the _____ is to genocide.
Final Solution

6. May 8, 1945, is to Germany as August 10, 1945, is to _____.
Japan

Part B
Complete each statement with the explanations given in your text.

1. The Nazis subjected Slavic peoples to brutal wartime measures **because**
**Possible answer: they considered them to be "inferior" people and
wanted to use their slave labor to help the German war effort.**

2. In July of 1942, the Germans began another offensive in the Soviet Union **because**
**Possible answer: they wanted to reach the Caucasus Mountains and
gain control of the Soviet Union's food and oil supplies.**

3. The battle of Stalingrad was significant **because**
**Possible answer: the Germans lost 350,000 troops and were forced
to retreat as the Soviet army took the offensive in eastern Europe.**

4. Stalin was suspicious when England and France did not immediately open a
second front in Europe **because**
**Possible answer: he thought these capitalistic countries were willing
to let the Soviet Union exhaust itself fighting the Germans.**

5. In 1945 Stalin decided to end his policy of neutrality toward Japan **because**
**Possible answer: Roosevelt promised Stalin territorial concessions
in Asia in return for his assistance.**

WORKSHEET
Chapter 35, Section 1

After World War II

Part A
Complete each statement with the explanations given in your text.

1. By 1950 the United Nations Security Council was paralyzed **because**
   Possible answer: the Soviet Union frequently used its absolute veto to block action by the council.

2. After World War II, the Soviet Union and the United States became superpower nations **because**
   Possible answer: both had survived the war with strength unmatched by any other nation.

3. Despite its limitations, the United Nations is a valuable organization **because**
   Possible answer: it serves as a forum for discussion and as an opportunity for nations to attack world problems jointly.

Part B
Imagine that you are the head of a newly independent nation. You are deciding whether or not to join the United Nations. Make a list of three reasons for belonging to the United Nations. Below are some details about your country that may help you make your decision.

- Your nation is subject to severe droughts.
- You must negotiate with France over control of an island claimed by your country.
- Your country has little industry; it exports some foodstuffs.
- In the past your country has gone to war with two of its neighbors.
- One of your neighboring nations is ruled by a tyrant; many refugees have poured into your country.

Students' answers may note that participation in the UN could give the new nation standing in the world community; the World Court could help in the conflict with France; the Economic and Social Council could help with the development of industry, the refugee problem, and the drought problem.

140   *Worksheets for History and Life*   © Scott, Foresman and Company

WORKSHEET

In this worksheet you will review the Cold War.

Chapter 35, Section 2

The Cold War in Europe

Part A

Use information from your text to complete the chart.

Cold War Terminology

Term	Definition	Example(s)
Cold War	**the increasingly hostile relationship between the United States and the Soviet Union after World War II**	the Soviet blockade of Berlin and the U.S. airlift of food; the formation of NATO and the Warsaw Pact
satellite	**nation that came under Soviet domination after World War II**	Poland, Bulgaria, Hungary, Czechoslovakia, Romania, East Germany
Truman Doctrine	military aid program for nations threatened by armed minorities or outside pressures	U.S. aid to Greece and Turkey, the Berlin airlift, formation of NATO, Marshall Plan
blockade	**cutting off of supplies**	**Soviet action in Berlin in 1949**

Part B

Write **C** next to each phrase that correctly completes the unfinished sentence. (Each incomplete sentence may have more than one correct ending.)

1. The Yalta agreement divided Germany into four zones jointly governed by

   C the Soviet Union.

   C the United States.

   C France.

   C Britain.

   _____ China.

2. After World War II, the Soviet Union wanted

   C heavy reparations from Germany.

   _____ favorable treaty terms for Italy.

   _____ economic assistance for Germany.

   C only friendly communist countries on its western border.

WORKSHEET
Chapter 35, Section 3

Soviet Cold War Policies

Part A
Identify the leader of the Soviet Union under whom the event took place by writing **S** for Stalin, **K** for Khrushchev, **B** for Brezhnev, and **G** or Gorbachev.

1. __K__ launch of first satellite
2. __B__ invasion of Czechoslovakia
3. __K__ first nuclear test ban treaty
4. __G__ introduction of *perestroika*
5. __K__ de-Stalinization speech
6. __K__ Hungarian uprising
7. __G__ introduction of *glasnost*
8. __S__ Yalta decisions and five-year plans
9. __K__ U-2 incident
10. __B__ outlawing of the labor union Solidarity
11. __K__ building of Berlin Wall
12. __K__ Cuban missile crisis
13. __S__ establishment of Soviet domination over all countries of Eastern Europe

Part B
Fill in the blanks with the word or words that best complete each sentence.

No country suffered more from World War II than did the __Soviet Union__.
Stalin wanted to restore the Soviet economy with two five-year plans that concentrated
on rebuilding __industry__. Although __consumer__ goods
were scarce, the __population__ increased. Stalin reimposed the harsh
__totalitarian__ controls of the 1930s and established Soviet domination of
the countries of __Eastern__ Europe. However, __Yugoslavia__,
led by Josip Broz, who called himself __Tito__, resisted Soviet control.
Angered by this show of independence, Stalin cut off all Soviet __economic aid__
to that country.

WORKSHEET
Chapter 35, Section 4

In this worksheet you will review events related to the United States during the 1950s and 1960s.

Prosperity and Social Change

Part A
For each pair of words, write a sentence that clearly explains the relationship between the two.

1. segregation/civil rights movement
   Possible answer: One goal of the civil rights movement was the end of segregation in schools, transportation, and other public facilities.

2. Mahatma Gandhi/Rev. Dr. Martin Luther King, Jr.
   Possible answer: Civil rights leader Rev. Dr. Martin Luther King, Jr. adopted Mahatma Gandhi's methods of nonviolent protest.

3. 1954 Supreme Court decision/schools
   Possible answer: The 1954 Supreme Court decision to desegregate public schools was a major victory for the civil rights movement.

4. GNP/goods and services
   Possible answer: GNP, or Gross National Product, is the total value of all goods and services that a country produces in a given year.

5. Civil Rights Act of 1964/peaceful protest
   Possible answer: After the Rev. Dr. King led a series of peaceful protests, Congress passed the Civil Rights Act in 1964.

6. GNP/prosperity
   Possible answer: An increase in GNP was one indication of American economic prosperity in the period after World War II.

Part B
Some people believe that the Korean War accomplished almost nothing. Write an essay in which you agree or disagree with this point of view.
Possible answer, agree: Little changed as a result of the war—the 38th parallel remains the line dividing North and South Korea, North Korea remains communist, and the area remains a trouble spot.
Possible answer, disagree: The war was a victory for Truman's containment policy because it stopped communist aggression.

WORKSHEET
Chapter 35, Section 5

In this worksheet you will review recent events in Western Europe.

Recent History of Western Europe

Part A
Identify the country described in the sentence.

1. War with Algeria almost created a civil war in this nation.   **France**

2. Francisco Franco was the dictator of this country until 1975.   **Spain**

3. Konrad Adenauer laid the foundation for democracy in this nation after World War II.   **West Germany**

4. In the 1970s and 1980s, this nation had the highest rate of inflation of all industrial nations.   **Britain**

5. This country withdrew its troops from NATO in 1966.   **France**

6. Two years after a military coup overthrew the dictator, this nation became a democracy.   **Portugal**

7. This country suffered economic isolation because its government supported the Axis during World War II.   **Spain**

8. Antonio Salazar was dictator of this nation for over 40 years.   **Portugal**

Part B
Present at least two specific facts from your text to support each statement.

1. The British economy became a mixture of free enterprise and socialism after World War II.
   Possible answer: The Labour government placed the Bank of England, coal mines, iron and steel works, communications and transportation systems, and electric and gas utilities under public ownership. Four-fifths of the economy remained in private hands.

2. Britain had to cope with continuing troubles in Northern Ireland.
   Possible answer: In 1969 violence broke out in Northern Ireland between the Protestant majority and the Roman Catholic minority. An extremist Catholic group, the IRA, launched a campaign of terrorism that was met with Protestant terrorism.

3. President De Gaulle was a French nationalist.
   Possible answer: De Gaulle refused to follow the American lead and developed an independent foreign policy. To ensure France's control over French military forces, he withdrew French troops from the joint NATO command.

WORKSHEET

Chapter 36, Section 1

In this worksheet you will review changes Mao Zedong and his successors brought to China.

Changes in China Since World War II

Part A
Write **T** if the statement is true and **F** if it is false. On the lines below, rewrite each false statement to make it true.

1. __T__ One reason that the communist revolution triumphed in China was that the Communists had far more popular support than the Nationalists.

2. __F__ The "Great Leap Forward" was successful in helping China to meet the food needs of its growing population.

3. __T__ The communist government broke with Chinese tradition by giving men and women equal rights under law.

4. __F__ Mao started the "Great Cultural Revolution" in order to uproot the Confucian ideas which kept people tied to the old social order.

5. __T__ Mao believed that it was intellectuals who were responsible for the spread of materialistic, anti-communist ideas.

6. __T__ Mao's successors have been using different methods, but their ambition to transform China into a modern superpower remains the same as his was.

2. Possible answer: The Great Leap Forward failed because Mao set unrealistic agricultural goals, and the rural people did not adapt well to the commune system.

4. Possible answer: Mao started the Great Cultural Revolution because he feared that the people were losing their revolutionary spirit and were becoming too interested in material possessions.

Part B
Write the letter of the term from the box next to its identifying clue words.

1. __c__ agriculture, industry, military, science

2. __e__ collective control, free enterprise, incentives

3. __a__ purges, Red Guards, "true communism"

4. __b__ communes, decreased agricultural output, failure

5. __d__ animosity, border disputes, disagreements over doctrine

> **a.** "Great Cultural Revolution"
> **b.** "Great Leap Forward"
> **c.** Four Modernizations
> **d.** China's break with the Soviet Union
> **e.** "responsibility system" of 1979

WORKSHEET
Chapter 36, Section 2

The Japanese Miracle

In this worksheet you will examine economic growth in Japan.

Part A

Write the letter of the term or phrase from the box that best completes each sentence.

1. Japan has protected its industries by taxing __b__.

2. Government contributions to aid business, or __e__, have facilitated Japan's high rate of business growth.

3. The high rate of savings in Japan has provided __g__ for Japanese businesses.

4. Foreign goods have been made more expensive for Japanese buyers by __a__ on imports.

5. The Japanese government's active role in guiding business is an example of __c__.

6. The __d__ that exists between the United States and Japan has created tension between the two countries.

7. The so-called "Japanese Miracle" refers to Japanese __f__.

a. tariffs
b. imports
c. guided capitalism
d. trade imbalance
e. subsidies
f. economic progress
g. investment capital

Part B

Read the passage and answer the questions.

If the Japanese are to maintain their position in the world, there must be a steady growth in world trade and a decrease in barriers like tariffs and quotas. All nations are now more or less dependent on the rest of the world, some more so than others. Japan is rising in the "more" category.

Japan's "Economic Miracle" has greatly increased its dependence on the global economy. Most of the energy and raw materials which fuel Japanese enterprises, as well as the food on which the Japanese live, come from sources outside Japan. No major country is more dependent on global trade than is Japan. Open markets and global cooperation—these are essential if Japan is to maintain its dominant economic position.

1. In what sense is Japan economically "dependent"?
   Possible answer: Japan depends on other nations to supply its raw materials and food and to buy its manufactured goods.

2. Why does the author argue that high tariffs and quotas are not really in Japan's interests?
   Possible answer: High tariffs and quotas hamper trade, which Japan needs to maintain its prosperity.

3. Give an example of a good title for this reading.
   Examples: Japan's Dependence on Global Trade or Free Trade and Japanese Prosperity

WORKSHEET

Chapter 36, Section 3

In this worksheet you
will review the history
of Vietnam from 1946 to
the present.

Vietnam Since World War II

Using the numbers **1** through **7**, arrange the events in chronological order. On the
lines after each event, tell why it was an important happening.

__2__ The Geneva Accords were signed.
**Possible answer: The signing ended the war between France and
Ho Chi Minh's government, called for free elections for Vietnam,
and divided the nation into North and South Vietnam.**

__3__ North Vietnam, backed by the Soviet Union, supported the rebellion that
broke out against the South Vietnamese government.
**Possible answer: This support indicated that these nations wanted
to place all of Vietnam under communist rule.**

__6__ A cease-fire was signed in January, 1973.
Possible answer: American fighting in Vietnam ended.

__7__ The South Vietnamese government collapsed.
Possible answer: Vietnam was unified under communist rule.

__1__ Ho Chi Minh issued a proclamation of Vietnamese independence.
**Possible answer: The proclamation led to the outbreak of war
between France and Ho Chi Minh's Vietnamese followers.**

__5__ The United States began peace negotiations in Paris.
**Possible answer: This move showed the strength of the antiwar
movement in the United States and signaled American willingness
to end the war through negotiation rather than fighting.**

__4__ The United States sent financial aid, advisers, and arms to South Vietnam.
**Possible answer: American leaders believed that providing this aid
could prevent the spread of communism in Southeast Asia.**

WORKSHEET

Chapter 36, Section 4

South Asia Since 1945

In this worksheet you will review some important people and events in the recent history of South Asia.

Part A
Write the letter of the name or phrase from the box next to its description.

1. __f__ Indian nationalist hero, assassinated in 1948
2. __g__ prime minister of India troubled by Sikh rebellion
3. __h__ prime minister of Pakistan, elected in 1988
4. __c__ traditional class divisions in India
5. __d__ first prime minister of India
6. __e__ ethnic group from northern India
7. __a__ Pakistan president killed in a suspicious plane crash
8. __b__ majority group in India

a. General Mohammad Zia	d. Jawaharlal Nehru	g. Indira Gandhi
b. Hindus	e. Sikhs	h. Benazir Bhutto
c. caste system	f. Mohandas Gandhi	

Part B
Use the information from your text to complete the following sentences.

1. In 1945 Britain announced that its most valuable colony, _____ India _____, would be granted full independence.

2. Fearing that the Hindus might persecute them, the _____ Muslims _____ demanded an independent state of their own.

3. In 1947 the British established the two sovereign dominions of _____ India _____ and _____ Pakistan _____.

4. _____ Pakistan _____ was given two distinct regions, separated by 1,000 miles of Indian territory.

5. East Pakistan became _____ Bangladesh _____ in 1971.

6. _____ India _____ supported Bangladesh in its struggle for independence.

7. Early in the 1980s, the Sikhs began fighting for an independent state in the _____ Punjab _____ area of northern India.

8. Indira Gandhi sent troops to _____ Punjab _____ to put down the _____ Sikh _____ struggle for independence.

© Scott, Foresman and Company

WORKSHEET

Chapter 37, Section 1

African Culture and Nationalism

Write **T** if the statement is true and **F** if it is false. Rewrite each false statement to make it true.

1. __F__ Négritude was a popular mass movement that originated among the urban poor in the late 19th century.

2. __F__ As a general rule, the Europeans prepared their colonists for self-government by allowing them to play a role in the national governments.

3. __T__ The Great Depression of the 1930s stimulated African nationalism.

4. __T__ Because many Africans still identified themselves by their ethnic group or by their religion after nations were formed, conflicting loyalties often led to hostilities and civil wars.

5. __T__ Nkrumah opposed Britain's plan concerning the independence of the Gold Coast.

6. __T__ In reaction to criticism of his government, Nkrumah became increasingly intolerant and autocratic.

7. __F__ Nkrumah was voted out of office because he had lost the confidence of the people.

8. __F__ Ghana has enjoyed stable democratic government since Jerry Rawlings seized control of the government.

1. Possible answer: Négritude was an expression of black pride and cultural nationalism that originated with a small group of educated Africans during the 1920s and 1930s.

2. Possible answer: As a general rule, Europeans allowed the colonists to participate in government on the local level only.

7. Possible answer: Nkrumah was ousted from power by a military coup while he was visiting China.

8. Possible answer: Rawlings seized power by military coups, and his government has faced increasing criticism for alleged human rights violations.

_____

_____

_____

_____

_____

_____

WORKSHEET
Chapter 37, Section 2

In this worksheet you will review the history of seven African nations after they gained independence.

Recent African History

Part A
Complete each analogy.

1. Jomo Kenyatta is to free enterprise as Julius Nyerere is to ____**socialism**____.
2. Congo is to ____**Zaire**____ as Tanganyika and Zanzibar are to Tanzania.
3. Lagos is to Nigeria as Abidjan is to ____**Côte d'Ivoire**____.
4. Mengistu Haile Mariam is to Ethiopia as Idi Amin Dada is to ____**Uganda**____.
5. Katanga is to Zaire as Biafra is to ____**Nigeria**____.
6. ____**Nigeria**____ is to oil as Zaire is to copper and cobalt.

Part B
Illustrate each general statement by an example from the recent history of one of the African countries discussed in Section 2.

1. The Soviet Union and Cuba have involved themselves in recent African affairs.
   Example: The Soviet Union rushed Cuban troops to aid the government of Ethiopia in its civil war against ethnic secessionists.

2. The existence of divided ethnic groups has complicated the internal political affairs of many African nations.
   Examples: Nigeria has 250 ethnic groups and has experienced a civil war started by Ibo secessionists. Ethiopia experienced a civil war when its Tigre, Somali, and Eritrean minorities tried to secede.

3. During the 1970s and 1980s, Africans faced an enormous crisis brought about by drought and famine.
   Example: In Ethiopia more than 200,000 people starved to death during a drought in 1972–1973.

4. Many African nations turned in the late 1980s toward free enterprise economies as a solution to some of their economic problems.
   Example: Tanzania returned state-owned businesses to private hands and turned to free-market policies as a solution to shortages.

WORKSHEET
Chapter 37, Section 3

Nationalism in Southern Africa

In this worksheet you
will review the struggle
for black rule in southern
Africa.

Part A
Identify each person described.

1. poet, medical doctor, and Marxist guerrilla leader who became the first president of Angola

2. the first president of Mozambique, who installed a communist system that nationalized private plantations and established state farms

3. the prime minister of Rhodesia, who unilaterally declared Rhodesia independent of Britain

4. a black South African lawyer who was arrested and jailed for organizing political protests

5. the Anglican archbishop of South Africa who was awarded the Nobel Peace Prize in 1985 for advocating peaceful change in South Africa

Agostinho Neto

Samora Machel

Ian Smith

Nelson Mandela

Desmond Tutu

Part B
Complete each statement with the explanations given in your text.

1. Britain imposed a trade embargo on Rhodesia **because**
   Possible answer: it wanted to force Rhodesia to grant political rights to blacks before granting Rhodesia independence.

2. South Africa's decision to lift a few racial restrictions in the late 1970s did not appease the black majority **because**
   Possible answer: the basic principles of apartheid in South Africa remained intact.

3. A civil war broke out in Angola in the late 1970s **because**
   Possible answer: not all Angolans supported Agostinho Neto, a committed Marxist, as Angola's first president.

4. In Rhodesia, Robert Mugabe and other black nationalist leaders opposed the government of Ian Smith **because**
   Possible answer: Smith's white-dominated Rhodesian government did not allow political rights to the black majority.

5. In the 1970s and 1980s, Namibian nationalist guerrillas clashed with South African military units in Namibia **because**
   Possible answer: South Africa refused to grant independence to Namibia, a League of Nations mandate it received after World War I, until 1988.

WORKSHEET
Chapter 37, Section 4

Independence in North Africa

Part A
Use information from the text to complete each of the following sentences.

1. Most North Africans speak _____**Arabic**_____ and are of
_____**Arab**_____ or _____**Berber**_____ descent.

2. In the North African countries, as in the Sub-Saharan states, the
_____**Muslim**_____ religion predominates.

3. Algeria, Tunisia, and part of Morocco were colonies of _____**France**_____.

4. Libya, which had been an _____**Italian**_____ colony, was given its
independence by the United Nations in 1951.

5. The _____**OAU**_____ was formed to help solve inter-African
disputes and to promote economic cooperation.

6. _____**Colons**_____ were French settlers who came to Algeria in
the 19th century.

7. ___**Muammar el-Qaddafi**___ of Libya has been denounced by some nations for
interfering in the affairs of other nations and for supporting international terrorists.

8. Algeria has had several border disputes with _____**Morocco**_____.

Part B
Identify the North African country described in each sentence by writing **L** for Libya,
M for Morocco, **T** for Tunisia, and **A** for Algeria.

1. __**A**__ Of all its North African colonies, France most wanted to keep this one.

2. __**T**__ Its strong nationalist party worked peacefully for independence from
1934 to 1956.

3. __**A**__ Terrorism, counterterrorism, and torture marked this nation's struggle
for independence.

4. __**A**__ Immediately after independence, this nation's large European community
departed, allowing for land redistribution.

5. __**A**__ Its government after independence tried to implement a policy of
Islamic socialism.

6. __**L**__ Its leader after independence banned political organizations and promoted
people's committees.

7. __**L**__ Its troops often have attempted to destabilize neighboring countries.

8. __**M**__ This country had to gain independence from both France and Spain.

WORKSHEET
Chapter 38, Section 1

The Middle East

Part A
Choose words from the box to complete the chart.

```
            Language Groups in the Middle East

      Semitic              Turkic           Indo-Iranian

  Arabic      Hebrew            Farsi              Kurdish
```

Farsi	Arabic	Turkic	Hebrew

Complete the sentences.

1. The most widely spoken Semitic language in the Middle East is __Arabic__.

2. The Israelis and their Arabic neighbors are culturally related in that both speak __Semitic__ languages.

3. The second largest Middle Eastern language family is __Turkic__.

4. The principal language of Iran is __Farsi__.

5. A group of 5 million that has maintained a sense of identity as one people despite being ruled by four different governments has been unified by the __Kurdish__ language.

Part B
Write **C** next to each phrase that correctly completes the sentence. (Each incomplete sentence may have more than one correct ending.)

1. The Middle East has been

   __C__ the scene of the Iran-Iraq war of the 1980s.

   __C__ the playing field for Soviet-Western power rivalries.

   __C__ the birthplace of three major world religions.

   ____ a region where nations have enjoyed a long history of independence.

2. The concept of pan-Arabism

   ____ created the Sunni-Shiite split.

   __C__ developed in response to Western imperialism.

   ____ espoused the policy of "divide and conquer."

   __C__ viewed Arab unity as a way to prevent Western domination of Middle Eastern economies.

WORKSHEET
Chapter 38, Section 2

The Impact of Oil

In this worksheet you will review the impact of oil upon the Middle East.

Part A
Use the graph and table below and your text to complete the following exercises.

Estimated World Oil Production, 1986*

Arab OPEC		Non-Arab OPEC	
(Percent of World Production)			
Algeria	1.1%	Ecuador	0.5%
Iraq	3.2%	Gabon	0.3%
Kuwait	2.2%	Indonesia	2.2%
Libya	1.8%	Iran	3.2%
Qatar	0.6%	Nigeria	2.6%
Saudi Arabia	8.4%	Venezuela	3.0%
United Arab			
Emirates	5.1%		
Total	**22.4%**	**Total**	**11.8%**

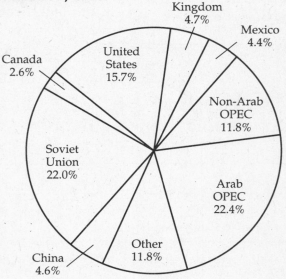

1. Which Middle Eastern OPEC nations listed were among the original countries that founded OPEC in 1960?
   Saudi Arabia, Kuwait, Iraq, and Iran

2. Which OPEC nation produced the most oil in 1986?
   Saudi Arabia

3. How does the oil production of the Arab OPEC nations compare with that of the non-Arab OPEC nations? What significance might this have?
   Possible answer: The Arab OPEC nations produce almost twice as much oil as the non-Arab OPEC members, which probably gives them great influence in setting OPEC policies.

Part B
Write the letter of the item from the box that best completes each sentence.

The recent increase in oil production has brought both economic and social changes. For one thing, rapid __f__ has occurred, often overwhelming local services. Women have benefited in that many now can find __e__ in the cities.

   Ironically, this very improvement in women's rights has triggered a growth in Islamic __a__. Some Westerners find it surprising that even modern Moslem women choose to wear the __d__. Less surprising is the fundamentalist opposition to Western values such as __b__. The clash between Western and __c__ views is likely to continue.

| a. fundamentalism |
| b. materialism |
| c. traditional |
| d. chadur |
| e. newly-created jobs |
| f. urbanization |

*Data from "The Worldwide Report," by *Oil and Gas Journal*, December, 22-20, 1986.

WORKSHEET
Chapter 38, Section 3
Arab-Israeli Conflict

In this worksheet you will review the historic development of Arab-Israeli hostility.

Part A
Label the map with the letter of each item from the box.

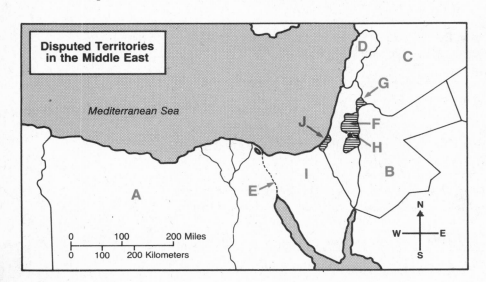

Disputed Territories in the Middle East

Mediterranean Sea

0   100   200 Miles
0 100 200 Kilometers

A. Egypt
B. Jordan
C. Syria
D. Lebanon
E. Suez Canal
F. West Bank
G. Golan Heights
H. Jerusalem
I. Sinai Peninsula
J. Gaza Strip

Part B
Complete each statement with the explanations given in your text.

1. Jews came to Palestine after World War II **because**
   Possible answer: they viewed Palestine as their ancient homeland.
   _____

2. The UN recommended that Palestine be partitioned **because**
   Possible answer: both Jews and Arabs wanted to dominate the government.

3. After the 1948 war, many Arabs from Palestine became refugees in camps in the West Bank, Gaza, and nearby Arab countries **because**
   Possible answer: Israel refused to allow the refugees to return to their homes in what had become Israel.

4. An *intifada* broke out in the Occupied Territories in 1987 **because**
   Possible answer: the Palestinian Arabs had become frustrated at Israel's lack of response to their grievances.

5. The Israelis did not want the Occupied Territories to become an independent Arab state **because**
   Possible answer: they feared that such a state on the West Bank would threaten Israel's security.

WORKSHEET

Chapter 38, Section 4

Political Development

In this worksheet you will review the recent history and important leaders of some Middle Eastern nations.

Part A

Identify the political leader who would be most likely to make or agree with each of the following statements by choosing the correct name from the box.

1. The Soviet Union is a useful ally. By cultivating Soviet friendship, one breaks the hold that the Western imperialists retain over our people.
Gamal Abdel Nasser

2. Unity, freedom, and socialism are our goals.
Hafez al-Assad

3. Death to America! Down with all those who act in collusion with the great Satan!
Ayatollah Khomeini

4. Modernization is the key to prosperity. It is time for women to take their rightful places in society. Factories and schools will aid us to cast aside the backwardness of the past.
Muhammad Reza Pahlavi

5. The Soviet military presence in Egypt and the eastern Mediterranean is deeply disturbing. The Soviets must leave!
Anwar Sadat

Anwar Sadat	Gamal Abdel Nasser	Muhammad Reza Pahlavi
Ayatollah Khomeini	Hafez al-Assad	

Part B

Identify the country to which each phrase refers by writing **IQ** for Iraq, **IR** for Iran, **IS** for Israel, **SA** for Saudi Arabia, **T** for Turkey, and **SY** for Syria.

1. **IR** in 1979 overthrew a monarchy that had taken steps to better the status of women

2. **IR** faced international condemnation for its use of poorly armed, poorly prepared boys as combatants

3. **IS** developed a multi-party democracy

4. **SY** since 1963 ruled by Baath party

5. **T** returned to democracy between episodes of military intervention in government

6. **SA** assumed a leadership role in OPEC

7. **IS** intended to form a self-sufficient, agricultural society

8. **IQ** ruled by the iron hand of dictator Saddam Hussein

WORKSHEET
Chapter 39, Section 1

In this worksheet you will review facts and opinions about Latin America's past development.

A Look at Latin America's Past

Part A
Read the statements and write **F** for fact and **O** for opinion.

1. __F__ The land in most Latin American countries is not equally distributed.

2. __F__ Latin American countries have a high rate of population growth.

3. __O__ Latin Americans have always valued large families.

4. __F__ Prior to World War II, most wealthy landowners in Latin America resisted land reform efforts.

5. __F__ One reason why many Latin American cities have grown is that rural families have moved to urban areas in the hope of finding jobs.

6. __O__ Most peasants who migrated to South American cities would have been better off had they remained in rural villages.

7. __O__ One reason why a strong feminist movement did not develop in Latin America was that most women were happy with their position in society.

8. __F__ Women in Latin America gained political rights later than women in the United States.

9. __O__ Latin Americans could not help but resent the foreign control of their resources.

10. __F__ Most Latin American countries had agricultural economies based on the export of only one agricultural product.

Part B
Select two of the statements you identified above as factual statements. Present at least two specific examples from your text to support each statement.
Examples:

2. **The population growth rate in Latin America is the highest in the world. The population of Latin America more than quadrupled between 1930 and the late 1980s.**

8. **Latin American women obtained the right to vote 10 to 20 years later than women in the United States; with the exception of Isabella Perón, Latin American women have not held important political office.**

WORKSHEET

Chapter 39, Section 2

Mexican and Cuban History

Part A
Number the events in each set in the order in which they happened.

Set 1

__2__ A new constitution called for many reforms, including universal suffrage and land reform.

__4__ Lázaro Cárdenas redistributed land and improved rural living standards.

__3__ The Institutional Revolutionary Party came to power.

__1__ A popular revolution overthrew dictator Porfirio Díaz.

__5__ Mexicans developed tourism and the oil industry.

Set 2

__3__ The Bay of Pigs invasion failed, and diplomatic relations were broken between Cuba and the United States.

__5__ The Cuban missile crisis caused even greater deterioration in U.S.-Cuban relations.

__2__ Fidel Castro seized properties belonging to U.S. citizens.

__1__ Dictator Fulgencio Batista fled into exile.

__4__ Castro declared Cuba a socialist state and accepted aid from the Soviet Union.

Part B
Identify each person described.

1. Mexican president overthrown in 1911 revolution

2. Mexican president who carried out extensive land reform in the 1930s

3. corrupt dictator overthrown in the Cuban revolution of 1959

4. Cuban leader who accepted Soviet economic aid

Porfirio Díaz
Lázaro Cárdenas
Fulgencio Batista
Fidel Castro

Part C
Why do you think U.S. relations with Cuba have been more troubled in recent decades than U.S. relations with Mexico?

Possible answer: Mexico and the United States share similarities in their political and economic systems. Cuban-U.S. relations deteriorated because of the Bay of Pigs invasion, the Cuban missile crisis, Cuba's relationship with the Soviet Union, and Cuban support for revolutionary groups in Africa and Latin America.

WORKSHEET

Chapter 39, Section 3

Argentina, Chile, and Brazil

In this worksheet you will review the recent history and current problems of three large South American nations.

Part A
Write **C** next to each phrase that correctly completes the sentence. (Each incomplete sentence may have more than one correct ending).

1. Juan Perón was able to seize power in Argentina partly because

   __C__ he settled strikes.

   __C__ he made friends with labor leaders.

   __C__ he had the help of other army officers.

   _____ he was supported by Argentina's leading landowners.

2. After gaining control of the government in Chile, Augusto Pinochet

   __C__ practiced successful economic policies that lowered inflation.

   __C__ headed a dictatorship of a small group of military leaders.

   __C__ used terror and intimidation against his regime's critics.

   __C__ restricted freedom of speech, dissolved the national congress, and abolished civil liberties.

3. Serious problems during Juan Perón's dictatorship included

   __C__ neglect of agriculture.

   __C__ runaway inflation.

   _____ nationalization of the copper mines.

   __C__ brutal suppression of opponents and attacks on the Roman Catholic Church.

4. Brazil appears to have the potential to become a powerful nation because it

   _____ continues to rely on a one-crop economy to support its growth.

   __C__ has made great progress in crop diversification and industrialization.

   _____ has experienced the complete absence of racial discrimination.

   __C__ has valuable natural resources and more than half of the South American population.

Part B
Write **T** if the statement is true and **F** if it is false. On the lines below, rewrite each false statement to make it true.

1. __T__ The military is a powerful force in Latin American political life.

2. __F__ Most 20th-century Latin American leaders have come to power through free and democratic elections.

3. __T__ Some leaders have used their dictatorial powers to take away the rights of their political opponents.

4. __F__ Both Juan Perón of Argentina and Augusto Pinochet of Chile had records of safeguarding human rights.

2. Possible answer: Some 20th-century Latin American leaders, including Juan Perón of Argentina and Getúlio Vargas of Brazil, have come to power through military takeovers.

4. Possible answer: Both Perón and Pinochet jailed, tortured, and executed their opponents.

WORKSHEET

Chapter 39, Section 4

In this worksheet you will review recent events in several Central American nations.

Central American Problems

Part A

For each statement below, write two or three sentences that support or provide details for that statement.

1. Costa Rica is an exception among the Central American nations.
   Possible answer: Unlike other Central American nations, Costa Rica never had a wealthy class of landowners. Today its economy is based on family-sized farms in rural areas and successful businesses in urban areas. In contrast, the economies of other Central American nations combine extremes of wealth and poverty.

2. The Somoza government antagonized many Nicaraguans during its years in power.
   Possible answer: The Somoza government was corrupt and ruthless. It antagonized the common people by its ruthlessness, corruption, granting of special privileges to friends and relatives of the Somozas, and use of dictatorial powers.

3. Statistics reveal that serious social and economic problems exist in most of Central America.
   Possible answer: Millions of children have little or no opportunity to attend school. Most Central Americans are poor; the average Honduran, for example, makes only barely enough to survive. Most people have no health care and the infant death rate is high.

Part B

Write the letter of the item from the box next to its identifying phrase.

1. __c__ revolutionaries who overthrew Anastasio Somoza in 1979
2. __d__ scene of U.S. marine interventions in 1912 and 1926
3. __a__ weapon used by the U.S. against the Sandinista government
4. __g__ Marxist opposition group in El Salvador
5. __f__ president of El Salvador's Revolutionary Government Council
6. __b__ a sudden seizure of political power
7. __e__ president of Nicaragua, elected in 1984

a. embargo on trade
b. coup d'état
c. Sandinistas
d. Nicaragua
e. Daniel Ortega
f. José Napoleón Duarte
g. Democratic Revolutionary Front

WORKSHEET
Chapter 39, Section 5

In this worksheet you
will review U.S.-Latin
American relations.

Foreign Policy Issues

Part A
Write **T** if the statement is true and **F** if it is false. On the lines below, rewrite each
false statement to make it true.

1. __T__ The United States dates its presence in Latin American affairs from its
victory over Spain in the Spanish-American War of 1898.

2. __F__ Most Latin Americans approved of the expansionist foreign policy
pursued by the United States in the early 20th century.

3. __F__ The United States will always control the Panama Canal.

4. __T__ Latin America, with its great natural resources, has been attractive to
American business interests.

5. __T__ During the Reagan years, U.S. foreign policy in Latin America attempted
to undermine communist influence in Latin America.

6. __F__ Only one city in the United States has a sizable Hispanic population.

**2. Possible answer: Most Latin Americans worried about this policy,
which they considered meddling in their affairs.**

**3. Possible answer: In 1978 the U.S. Senate signed a treaty that returns
control of the canal to Panama in 1999.**

**6. Possible answer: New York, Chicago, Los Angeles, San Antonio, and
Miami all have sizable Hispanic populations.**

Part B
Explain why each of the following U.S. Presidents would have disagreed with the
statement: The United States should view Latin America as a ripe economic plum
waiting to be picked.

1. Franklin Roosevelt
**Possible answer: Franklin Roosevelt pursued Latin American
friendship in the hope of reducing the possible influence of Nazi
Germany in the region. His Good Neighbor policy encouraged
economic development in Latin America.**

2. Ronald Reagan
**Possible answer: Although Ronald Reagan wanted to stop the
extension of communist influence in Latin America, he did not seek
direct economic advantages for the United States in the region.**

WORKSHEET
Chapter 40, Section 1

The World Economy

In this worksheet you will review some economic issues of international importance.

Part A

For each set of statements below, write **M** before the main idea and **S** before statements that support or help explain the main idea. One statement in each set is not related to the main idea; write **X** next to this statement.

Set 1

__S__ Industrialized and developing nations are tied to each other economically.

__S__ Multinational corporations have business operations in a number of different countries.

__M__ The world has become economically interdependent.

__S__ The highly competitive world market has fostered the development of a global economy.

__X__ Population growth has cancelled out economic growth in many countries.

Set 2

__M__ Communist countries have experienced difficulties competing in world markets.

__S__ The goods produced in communist countries have often been poor in quality.

__X__ There are few communist countries in the Western Hemisphere.

__S__ Few noncommunist nations have bought the inferior goods produced in communist nations.

__S__ The state-controlled communist economies have produced a limited amount of consumer goods.

Part B

Read the paragraph and answer the questions that follow.

By the end of 1988, developing countries had accumulated over $1.2 trillion dollars in debt to industrial countries. The debt crisis emerged in the early 1980s when several of the largest debtors in Latin America found themselves unable to repay their debts. Their inability to repay their loans has stemmed in part from problems in the world economy that adversely affected their exports and domestic policies that discouraged economic growth. The failure of countries to repay their loans discouraged commercial banks in industrial countries from making further loans to these countries. The slowdown in lending, in turn, prevented many developing countries from making investments needed to strengthen their economies and improve their ability to repay their loans. The developing countries found themselves in a difficult situation. By repaying their loans to industrialized countries, developing nations severely restricted their ability to invest at home and improve their economic status; however, a refusal to pay jeopardized their ability to borrow from industrialized nations in the future.

1. According to the reading, what difficult situation faces developing countries?
   Possible answer: They are forced to choose between debt repayment and economic growth, but cannot have one without the other.

2. What are two reasons that some Latin American nations encountered difficulties repaying their debts?
   Possible answer: The value of their exports declined due to world market conditions; domestic policies discouraged economic growth.

3. Should a country default on its loans, how would this affect its economy?
   Possible answer: The nation would receive fewer loans for investment in the future and would be less able to strengthen its economy.

WORKSHEET
Chapter 40, Section 2

In this worksheet you will review the environmental challenges facing our global society today.

The Challenge of the Environment

Part A

Petroleum and natural gas are energy resources that could be exhausted within the next century. However, alternative sources of energy have various limitations. On the lines below, describe the limitations of each energy source.

1. coal
    Coal is costly to refine. Burning coal pollutes the air.
    _____

2. hydroelectric power
    Hydroelectric plants require a suitable location, are expensive to build, and create environmental problems.

3. nuclear power
    Construction costs can be prohibitive. Nuclear reactor accidents are serious worries.

Part B

Use information from the text to complete the following sentences.

1. Other countries followed the lead of the superpowers and developed nuclear weapons **because**
    Possible answer: they believed nuclear weapons were necessary for their national security.

2. The SALT I treaty was important **because**
    Possible answer: it showed the superpowers' concern about the buildup of nuclear weapons.

3. The INF treaty could be viewed as a sign of improved relations between the two superpowers **because**
    Possible answer: their agreement to destroy intermediate-range missiles showed that both sides wanted to avoid nuclear war.

4. Fear of nuclear weapons increased during and after the Cuban missile crisis of 1962 **because**
    Possible answer: the crisis showed how close superpowers could come to a nuclear confrontation.

5. Recently the potential danger of nuclear weapons being used in regional conflicts has increased **because**
    Possible answer: more and more nations—an estimated 20 by 1990—have their own atomic bombs.

WORKSHEET

Chapter 40, Section 3

Three Views of the Future

In this worksheet you will review three futurist views and their strategies for resource utilization.

Part A

Identify the world view associated with each of the following statements by writing **M** for Malthusian, **E** for expansionist, and **EC** for ecological. A statement may be associated with more than one world view.

1. **M** Eventually human intervention will push nature to its limits, with disastrous consequence.

2. **EC** The realization of human rights and conditions of political justice are important for meeting challenges of the future.

3. **E** New technologies will enable us to accomplish more in the future with fewer resources.

4. **M, EC** A fundamental shift in values will be necessary to meet the challenges of the future.

5. **M, EC** The world of the future requires a world government.

6. **E** The problems created by technology can be corrected by still better technology.

7. **EC** Humanity cannot stand apart from nature.

8. **E** Breakthroughs in nuclear, thermonuclear, and solar energy will provide an almost indefinite supply of power.

9. **EC** Our major objectives should be to conserve natural resources and to distribute the world's resources equitably.

10. **M** For the world to survive there must be drastic population reductions in all nations, particularly in the developing ones.

Part B

Read the statements below and write **F** for fact and **O** for opinion before each one. For each opinion, explain one other point of view that people might hold.

1. **F** Living standards rose dramatically as a result of 19th-century industrialization.

2. **O** Technology will enable us to eliminate world poverty.

3. **F** Malthus believed that the problems of his time were the result of humanity's predestined need to alter nature through science and technology.

4. **O** An international organization such as the United Nations should be given the authority to manage and distribute the world's resources.

2. Example: Those who control the use of technology have ignored—and will continue to ignore—the problem of poverty.

4. Example: Smaller governments, such as those on the national and local level, can best ensure use of resources in a manner consistent with cultural uniqueness.